Philosophy of Science

This book is one of a series, Traditions in Philosophy, published by Pegasus in cooperation with Educational Resources Corporation, which has developed and created the series under the direction of Nicholas Capaldi, Professor of Philosophy, Queens College, New York.

Philosophy of Science
AN INTRODUCTION

Robert Ackermann

PEGASUS NEW YORK

Library of Congress Catalog Card Number 79–110438

"If a photon could talk, we could not
understand it."

—Jack Kelly

Contents

Preface   page ix–xi

Part One
The Methodology of Science

ONE ☐ The Philosophy of Science 17
TWO ☐ The History of Science 26
THREE ☐ The Logic of Science 40
FOUR ☐ The Evolution of Science 54

Part Two
Science Fiction

FIVE ☐ Foundations 78
SIX ☐ Space and Time 101
SEVEN ☐ Life 128

Further Reading 150
Bibliography 159
Index 165–168

Preface

I once knew a man who always worried that the roof of any room which he occupied was likely to fall in and injure or kill him. This worry was, in a sense, philosophical; no one could *prove* that the worry was without foundation in fact. But instead of being regarded as a philosopher, this worrier was thought of as a harmless lunatic, known among intimates as "Crazy Phil." There is an uncomfortable resemblance between Crazy Phil and many philosophers of science. Like Phil, these philosophers are motivated by private fears. They worry that scientific practice does not conform to certain personal philosophical criteria of adequacy. This worry can be translated into the activity of pursuing various philosophical programs, e.g., a philosopher may try to construct scientific knowledge out of sense-data, or solely out of statements about the observable properties of observable individuals. One cannot help but feel a certain tolerance for such activity. It can be regarded as interesting or amusing in a zany way, like the activity of a hobbyist who attempts construction of a locomotive out of matchsticks. The matchstick locomotive won't move, nor pull a train, in spite of its mimicry of the correct shape, and similarly none of the philosophical constructions seem even to begin to illustrate the dynamics of scientific practice. Hobbyists are not usually unaware of the distinction between their models and the real object. Philosophers, on the other hand, being eccentric on a grander scale, have sometimes taken their constructions to be constitutive of sound scientific practice, refusing to allow the term *science* (in its full glory) as descriptive of any activity not conforming to the features of *their* models.

Part One of this book will be concerned with sketching out some main threads which may be used to find a pattern in the literature of contemporary philosophy of science. Philosophers have written from so many personal perspectives and with so many diverse goals that it is not easy even to begin an exposition of their collective contributions. I will therefore plainly state at the conclusion of this paragraph the large perspective from which this account will view the relevant literature. It should be noted that no comparable problem of perspective exists in reviewing the literature of the sciences. Anyone can see that accurate descriptions of the weather in conjunction with an accurate method of forecasting the weather from such descriptions would be an obvious desideratum for society. The only question is whether the weather can be accurately described and accurately forecast, and the only material relevant to answering the question is an examination into current and past methods, and an assessment of their success. In a way, anyone can see that an accurate description of the dynamics of good scientific practice is also a desideratum for such purposes as educating scientists and allocating funds in a society. The question, once again, is whether accurate descriptions of scientific practice and methods of forecasting the direction and nature of sound scientific practice are possible. As before, the material relevant to answering the question lies in an examination of current (and past) accounts. Here, however, the patent influence of human creativity gives rise to a nearly irresistible urge to suppose that no forecasting is possible. Human creativity makes it impossible to forecast individual discoveries or individual practice. The problem is really to see whether an appropriate level of description and forecasting can lead to interesting explanatory patterns for sound scientific practice.

In this book, the question has been explored by taking quite seriously an analogy between the development of scientific practice in specific areas of scientific theorizing and the evolutionary development of a biological species. At root, the point of doing this is based on the contention that although mutation, the activities of predators and so on, may preclude biological forecasting of individual biographies, interesting explanatory patterns are found in evolutionary theory at an appropriate level of analysis. The analogy is used to provide a touchstone for the literature of philosophy of science in Part One.

In Part Two, more explicit development of the analogy is undertaken with reference to some specific scientific problems. Part Two will seem hopelessly speculative and obscure to many, but there is sufficient justification for this style of attack given in the history of philosophy. I should not myself like to see it disappear.

In citing literature, I have been very selective. To begin with, any effort to provide a comprehensive bibliography within the limitations of this monograph would have threatened the appearance of any text. I have therefore merely cited some representative and easily accessible books and articles that seem to me both interesting and moderately permanent. Anyone who looks at these will quickly find entrance to the total literature which lies in the background.

I should like to acknowledge here my very great debt to John C. "Jack" Kelly for demonstrating the superiority of the well-timed laugh to the gape of astonishment as an argumentative weapon, and for extremely patient and stimulating discussion of diverse philosophical issues. I hope he will find the time to work on his irons and get down to scratch, and the repudiation of some of his views implicit in what follows may be just the stimulus that he needs.

Robert Ackermann
Amherst, Massachusetts

Part One

The Methodology of Science

Introduction

The swift and common answer to any wonder at the obvious success of scientists in furnishing creature comfort and intellectual comprehension is to say that their success is rooted in a superior method of investigation. This can be elaborated by suggesting that scientific discovery (by contrast to the development of religious systems) is free from authoritarianism, self-correcting through free criticism and revision, and above all responsive to the nuances of accumulating data. Unfortunately for the easy answer, such an account is difficult to justify in terms of the facts of scientific history. It is not always the theologian who is obscurantist and authoritarian, nor always the scientist who eschews dogma and welcomes new data. Whatever the statistics about individuals, there are men to admire in both traditions, and for precisely the same intellectual qualities. In order to contend that there are features which can be regarded as constitutive of a distinctive scientific method, the philosopher is therefore forced into attempting exposure of rather subtle features of scientific practice which he discerns in a close analysis of various documents. As a result, the philosophy of science is essentially a *normative* study.

15

Rather than merely paraphrasing or reporting scientific practice, a philosopher who wishes to advance a thesis about the methodological superiority of science, or who merely wishes to understand an instinctive feeling that the scientific tradition contains features which set it apart from various other traditions, must find grounds for his views in an analysis of what he regards as *good* scientific practice by finding therein certain explanatory traits. Contrary to what may be naive supposition, the result of this method of investigating science is often that the philosophy of science as undertaken by professional philosophers contains much argument and analysis, but little actual science.

The first three chapters of Part One will survey some of the explanatory views about methods in science which have been proposed by various philosophers of science. In the last chapter, some views of the author will be advanced to suggest some relatively unexplored but interesting lines of development for a detailed analysis of sound scientific practice.

1

The Philosophy of Science

It is to be expected that philosophy should take as paradigmatic for various questions of epistemology and ontology the most extensive and coherent body of knowledge available to it. Mathematical and religious systems of knowledge have, in the past, furnished systems of coherent information against which philosophical speculation has been tested. The obvious scope and coherence of modern science has made it, since the seventeenth century, the major touchstone for assessing philosophical pronouncements about knowledge and existence.

In using science as a paradigm, however, philosophers have not been content to accept the latest opinions of reputable scientists as the sole criterion of knowledge. Scientific opinions often clash, and they are known to be unstable in the face of unexpected experimental data. A good philosophical view is somewhat more permanent, for a man cannot sustain the upheaval of deep-rooted beliefs every few months. Indeed, we see in the behavior of single scientists an aversion to change in certain fundamental concepts quite like that of nonscientists. Therefore, even if one holds a simplistic view that certain theories are usually accepted by nearly all scientists because of the nature of the evidence, it would turn out that an accurate account of scientific practice could not be a simple one of immediate accommodation of new data. A philosopher should be expected to find an appropriate damping mechanism for the oversimplified view that the latest opinions of top scientists constitute the paradigm of human knowledge.

One proposed damping mechanism with a venerable history is common sense. Common sense is a notoriously vague notion, but it has been revived in a vigorous form recently in the suggestion that a careful analysis of correct ordinary usage can set conceptual limits on what it is reasonable for a man to believe. It is easy to lampoon this outlook. Scientific history can provide many cases where conceptual limitations have been shown to be severely anthropomorphic in the light of new scientific discoveries. Flat earth views will no doubt serve as a non-controversial example. The appeal to ordinary usage, however, actually holds only that it is reasonable not to quickly abandon conceptual limitations which can be teased out of ordinary language, even if new experimental data seem inexplicable in terms of older concepts. Everyone can agree that scientific views clashing with common sense will be absorbed into the conceptual framework of ordinary language if they pass sufficiently sustained scientific scrutiny.

Reliance on common sense as a damping mechanism is appropriately related to traditional views of philosophy as a reflective, rather than a practical, discipline. Existing human institutions, even when they work poorly by some criteria, are nonetheless of proven viability. In terms of broad human political, ethical, and aesthetic interests, we can see in retrospect that the too hasty implementation of various scientific discoveries could well not have improved human life, but have rendered it more difficult, or even destroyed it. It does not require a philosopher to point out that this is too high a price to pay for the information that some hypothesis is false.

We should expect a sound philosophy of science to encourage the examination of new views carefully, without rushing to the conclusion that each new view compatible with the evidence must be an advance. It would seem that some philosophers have concluded from the overall advance of scientific knowledge seen on a grand scale that every tiny portion of scientific history embodying sound methodology or practice must be a forward thrust.

Philosophy of science in one aspect is a critique of current scientific opinions by comparison to proven past views, or in terms of criteria developed from such views, but such philosophy of science is clearly not a discipline autonomous of actual scientific practice. Scientists are going to criticize each other pretty severely anyway, whether or not philosophers undertake to urge criticism upon them. If a man knows enough to intelligently criticize reigning views in an area of science, we can call his critical activity philosophy of science, recognizing that whether the man is better regarded professionally as a philosopher or as a scientist is a moot point. This kind of critical philosophy of science cannot be easily distinguished from various problems of judgment and valuation associated with any theoretical problem. A more general philosophy of science would have to deal with issues about scientific knowledge cutting across wide domains of scientific activity.

While common sense may provide a suitable damping mechanism for scientific views in discussions of the social implementation of various scientific views, it is clear that it can play no extensive role as a damping mechanism in discussions of particular theoretical issues, or in a discussion of issues in general philosophy of science. In such discussions, an apparent appeal to common sense is likely to be an appeal to received scientific views or scientific practice, and such an appeal may bear little resemblance to the common-sense conceptual limits which have been discerned in ordinary language. A general philosophy of science, while not rejecting considerations of common sense, would have to be prepared to reject them in some cases of conflict with scientific belief, and to be prepared to discuss some exotic cases where common sense could furnish no suitable guidelines. This last case is sufficient to establish the point, and deserves some closer attention.

Traditional philosophical epistemology faced with the datum of scientific knowledge was usually concerned with extending its scope and style of analysis to ask how an objective scientific view could be held and defended by a single human being on the basis of his own experiences. Science has shifted the significance of the notion of an observer to include hypothetical observers having the property that they can exist at points, or inside stars, or before the appearance of planets (and man) in the universe. Although this shift is profound in its consequences for epistemology, the significance of the shift is rarely discussed by philosophers. Our percepts (and to a great extent our concepts) are dependent upon our development as biological organisms in a restricted natural environment. It is not surprising that the very small and the very large should seem paradoxical or inconsistent when observations of them need to be reported in terms of human speech and perceptual mechanisms. The scientific observer of the very large, for example, has to forsake perception of space and time as independent. Contrary to progressive philosophical opinion in some quarters, this does *not* mean that for philosophical purposes we need always chat knowingly about space-time by contrast to our benighted forebears. Should relativistic phenomena become a commonplace through repeated high-speed rocket travel or other means, we can expect our descendants to incorporate a satisfactory vocabulary and manner of speech.

The shift in view, as such scientific observers return increasingly abstract data, has forced philosophers of science to forsake ordinary language as a damping mechanism, a move which must be made as philosophy of science turns its attention from the impact of scientific discoveries on traditional philosophical questions to the direct analysis of scientific practice. This move to an analysis of practice has virtually created the branch of philosophy now known technically as the philosophy of science.

The direct analysis of scientific practice would hopefully produce logical models of the proper relationship between scientific theory and scientific data. These models, rather than common sense or analyses in terms of the conceptual structure of ordinary language, would then become the primary damping mechanism for introducing stability into the analysis of scientific practice.

There is a serious danger accompanying the use of logical models. Once a model has been constructed, it is easy for the philosopher to assume that an area of scientific practice not conforming to its properties is in a state of confusion or growth that will only be satisfactorily resolved when the features of the model can be met by virtue of an experimental or theoretical discovery. This stance can be no better than the model which is used for the testing. It is clear that a successful general logical model of the relationship between theory and data for any domain of scientific activity would have enormous valuable consequences for the strategy of scientific research and the curriculum of scientific education. The problem is not whether logical models would be a valuable philosophical contribution to the study of scientific practice, but rather whether useful ones can be constructed which possess any degree of comprehensiveness. The technical controversies of the philosophy of science have largely centered on the question of the properties and the scope of possible logical models and their relationship to actual scientific practice. These controversies will be reviewed in the remaining chapters of Part One.

To discuss the possibility of a general philosophy of science, it is necessary to raise some rather abstract issues concerning scientific practice. For example, we may reasonably expect to inquire into the possible goals of scientific activity on the natural assumption that it is in some way purposeful. It is sometimes said that the aim of science is to control nature, and sometimes that it is to understand nature. If we suppose that it is reasonable to ask, "What is the aim of science?" we are already perilously close to taking these viewpoints seriously as alternatives. But it is not difficult to see that man as a scientist is too curious to permit either viewpoint to be a completely satisfactory characterization. Let a man gain an understanding of some natural process or law and he will wonder how to put this understanding to use. Let a man gain control of some process and he will typically wonder at the fact of his control, i.e., he will look for an understanding of it. For practical or professional reasons, a man may suppress either impulse, but there is a sense in which both are obviously part of the immensely variegated skein of scientific activity.

The philosophical tradition has rather obviously been oriented toward activity or control. It is not surprising therefore that many philosophers have attempted to use a commonsense distinction between pure and applied science in order to carve out an area of inquiry. For these purposes, the two branches of science can be seen as an attempt to understand nature and as an attempt to control it. Having suitably sharpened this distinction, a philosopher might then naturally focus his attention on science as an attempt to understand nature. This preliminary step reduces the complexity of the problem of giving a general philosophical account of scientific activity, and there is nothing wrong with the reduction provided that the philosopher does not later forget that he had originally simplified the problem.

In this respect, philosophy of science may be compared with musical or literary criticism. A musical critic cannot evaluate every new record issued by a recording company in the United States, nor can a literary critic read every new novel issued by a publishing company. There is simply too much source material for criticism. To keep the job within bounds, some preliminary method of restricting the field of the critic's attention is required. Anyone restricting his attention in this way, even though it is by necessity, will miss some material that he might have found interesting had restriction and selection not been forced upon him. Now it is a commonplace that some critics attempt omniscience in the face of these facts by verbal play. Having restricted themselves to music which is, let us say, *serious* according to their selection criteria, they may then make the mistake of treating music as though all good music would have to be serious in the sense provided by the analysis. A philosopher of science should not forget that there is good science in a good experiment, or a good piece of engineering, even though his attention is restricted by the exigencies of his task to a certain kind of theoretical activity as a primary focus for analysis, a restriction which happens to fit his usual intellectual predilections fairly closely.

The limitations of the proposed logical models for assessing scientific activity should be carefully remembered. Philosophers like to consider theories, laws, hypotheses, and data as sentences or statements, and then look for a logical structure relating these statements. Such an analysis cannot be completed until appropriate sentences or statements are available for analysis, and this has to be after the period of discovery of the theories, and after the relevant experiments have been performed. A successful philosophical analysis resulting in a logical model for scientific practice then describes an ideal situation to be satisfied as a successful result of scientific practice, but it makes no pretense of describing a model for the dynamics of scientific history.

Returning to our critical metaphor, philosophy of science has so far most nearly approximated criticism of the kind that takes a poem, novel, composition, painting, or sculpture as a datum to be analyzed in terms of its internal structure, without reference to the intentions of the artist, or to his social surroundings. Such criticism can be extremely interesting, but it is not the only interesting kind of criticism. In practice, the philosophy of science is even more abstractive. Whereas individual works of art are a natural datum for analysis, the opinions of individual scientists usually are not. The choice of a datum for analysis in the philosophy of science is thus very important. In many cases, a textbook exposition of a theory used as a datum may be an amalgam of individual opinions which must be regarded merely as a consensus view intended for beginners. A textbook exposition does not, in many ways, correspond to actual scientific practice or belief. A philosopher of science must take care in selecting his data for analysis, an abstractive process which is often not noticed, or carried out in terms of insufficiently scrutinized implicit assumptions. One of the deepest criticisms of much of contemporary philosophy of science is that it has often lapsed into the critics battling the critics, resulting in a nearly complete separation of critical views from the practices which are ideally to be analyzed. Our analogy suggests that this is an occupational disease without a known vaccine.

Have we not arrived at the nub of the matter? Should not the critic master practice before he criticizes, and, if so, does not the time required for mastery preclude any remainder for his critical reflections? Scientists have sometimes exploited this situation in order to suggest that the philosophy of science must remain totally amateur and useless for scientific practice:

> (The scene is an academic cocktail party.)
> Scientist to philosopher: "Tell me something you've learned recently about science." (He laughs to himself quietly.)
> Philosopher: "Well—uh . . . ."

An aggressive and accomplished scientist can expect to win this one hands down against the front line for the philosophy of science, particularly if he is a physicist. The real difficulty is that science cannot be *mastered* in the appropriate sense, and "Master-scientist Bruce Wayne" is strictly comic-book stuff. The philosopher's moment comes as he watches the scientists battling it out at their own conferences. Academic life has fairly rigid conventions, some of which lead to tolerance of opinions from colleagues that would not be tolerated from students or unknown academics, particularly from another branch of the university structure. The interesting problem is to see whether a valid or even interesting general philosophy of science can be sought in spite of the academic pecking order.

Suppose, for example, that philosophy of science were banished for lack of grants. This would not end the critical activity suggested by our initial phrase *philosophy of science*. As we suggested, scientists could not help but continue to criticize other scientists and their work. It is not the existence of philosophy of science which is in question, but what kind of philosophy of science, or kinds of philosophy of science, can actually be valuable for scientific practice.* This is a deep problem on which we can expect variety of opinion, and no settled answers.

I should like to make the following preliminary suggestions. Scientists, in an important sense, are only human. In order to work effectively, they must see themselves as part of an on-going practice and institution whose general outlines they can comprehend. The intellectual qualities of good scientists are incompatible with contentment in the role of cogs in some unknown mechanism. The practice of individual scientists thus usually exhibits an implicit or explicit set of views which may be regarded as a philosophy of science. These philosophies would be expected to be highly colored by the successful methodologies of the area of science in which the individual scientist works. We may then expect to discern philosophies of science in the biographies of good scientists. The problem of the philosophy of science is whether these implicit philosophies of science can be assessed from any meaningful general standpoint not closely associated with the methodology of some particular area of scientific research.

Philosophy, in an important sense, is always connected with the concerns and the views of a single man. Supposed philosophical views too complicated for a single man to comprehend are simply not suitable regarded as philosophical views. On the other hand, we may expect that certain scientific views are beyond the comprehension of a single man. It is therefore a possible and intriguing prospect that a sufficiently wide philosophical perspective on scientific practice would reveal patterns and connections not easily recognizable by a single person engaged primarily in the activity. A philosopher, like a scientist, has to strike off on his own when he believes that he has absorbed enough instruction to provide a reasonable background for statement of his own opinions.

*This will seem crotchety to some, but I think it perfectly legitimate for a philosopher to satisfy his own intellectual curiosity about scientific practice by attempting to read about scientific practice, without supposing that his activity would have utilitarian consequences. Most philosophers of science have supported rather strong claims that the philosophy of science is of potential use to scientific practice, and such claims have to be evaluated in the marketplace.

2

The History of Science

The history of science has become a specialized discipline whose pursuit is not as entangled with the philosophy of science as one might expect. For it is quite possible to attempt a narrative or report of the career of some scientist, or of the development of an area of science, without attempting to find in the narrative any data for a general methodological study of scientific practice. In other words, the historian may rightfully attempt a sensitive reconstruction of what has happened, a reconstruction that will make the career or the development interesting and intelligible, without attempting to locate in the narrative the features of any supposed logical structure of sound scientific practice. Generally speaking, historians of science have been reluctant to suppose that a technical philosophy of science is really possible.

From the viewpoint of the philosophy of science, the history of science does not supply the appropriate data for possible generalization, even though philosophers may correctly suppose that the appropriate data are to be found in history. To begin with, a narrative based on scientific biography is likely to rely on such sources as the reminiscences of individual scientists, and these reminiscences have usually shown a personal perspective somewhat at odds with other such perspectives, and they have often contained anachronisms and at least apparent contradictions with other reminiscences of the same scientist at different times. If the data for a philosophy of science are to be obtained from such sources, a sufficiently sophisticated historical and philosophical method must be used to assess and structure the narrative account.

One may legitimately start an investigation of the narrative by looking to commonly recognized important developments in science, and the accounts provided by the biographies and the papers of the scientists who are associated with these developments. It seems reasonable to suppose that a competent scientist involved in theoretical rather than practical developments is likely to bring to bear some self-conscious philosophical and methodological sophistication. As we have suggested, scientists are not generally free in such situations from the constraints of an implicit philosophical view. It is not uncommon for a practicing scientist to absorb in his graduate training some methodological and even philosophical views which are sufficient for the pursuit of a relatively narrow line of research throughout a scientific career. These biographies, while part of science, are not likely to provide the data for a philosophy of science. A philosopher and historian may be interested to see whether he can tease out an *explicit* philosophical view which would provide some explanation of the relationships between the data, the hypotheses, the laws, and so on. An explanation would be provided if the actual development proceeded along lines which are explicable as good science in the explicit view, while false starts and potential developments are seen not to be. It may seem that seizing on generally recognized important developments is to write the history from a partial perspective, much as a history of the deeds of the kings of a country is only a partial history. But this can be defended, for the deeds of kings have been important for the development of their countries.

Some important philosophers of science who have pursued the analysis of specific scientific advances from an historical and philosophical perspective are N. R. Hanson, Stephen Toulmin, and Thomas Kuhn. These philosophers have been resistant to generalization from their historical studies, and their comments on methodology are often merely the presentation of philosophically analyzed examples, rather than the presentation of logical models for sound practice in general. The examples presented by these philosophers are not only intrinsically interesting for any attempt to study scientific practice, but they seem also to constitute the kind of data which could provide the criterion for a sound abstract conception of scientific methodology, if that is possible. At the present time, instead of leading to such an abstract conception, their examples seem rather to serve as counter-examples to the extent proposals for a general methodology of the kind that will be introduced in the next chapter.

We should not lose sight of the fact that it *is* possible to generalize about scientific practice if true statements about scientific practice are the sole desiderata. There is a description of scientific practice, true insofar as it goes, that is often presented in introductory science texts in some form similar to the following. A scientist begins his work with certain data germane to some problem. He then formulates various hypotheses which, if true, would solve the problem and account for the data. An experiment is then devised to discriminate among the rival hypotheses. The experiment is then performed, and the scientist ends this little episode by humbly accepting that hypothesis singled out by the experiment.

There are several problems with this scenario. Most obviously, it fails to distinguish good scientific practice from activity that we would not normally count as scientific. A champion housewife might follow this procedure in winning the blue-ribbon cookie recipe prize after repeated failure in the oven. Even more surprisingly, The Lone Ranger seems to be a scientist on this characterization, since the weekly episodes of his illustrious career exhibit these features of scientific practice. (His experiments are often performed in disguise.) As is well known, the highly motivated Lone Ranger hardly verifies one hypothesis before he is riding off to a new problem area. The failure of the overly inclusive simple description given above of scientific practice makes it tempting to conclude that scientific activity may be as much characterized by the problems to which it addresses itself as by the methodology which it exhibits under some philosophical analysis.

There is another difficulty with this brief characterization which is worth mentioning. In the classical days of the lone scientist, a single man did his own theorizing and experimenting. At present, the institutionalization of scientific activity has resulted in scientific teams, each member of which may perform but a specialized task. None of these tasks may exhibit all of the features of the previous description of scientific activity. A scientist may neither experiment nor theorize in any clear sense, yet be a good scientist for all of that. Therefore, the activity of a single individual scientist may receive its significance only in the context of a larger program involving a number of other individuals. To by-pass a hopelessly complicated discussion of the sociology of science, we will refer to scientific practice and suppose that sound scientific practice, even if the bits are shared among a number of different scientists, will conform to some general methodological description.

Clearly, even if some appeal is made to a notion of scientific practice, the description previously offered is not very convincing because of its failure to discriminate good scientific practice from bad scientific practice and from various nonscientific activities. The worth of scientific practice must be more clearly tied to the quality of the rival hypotheses introduced to explain the data than our description has so far suggested. Without presenting case histories from the works of the philosophers of science who have been interested in historical examples, I should like to suggest that their examples support some sharpening of the focus of this traditional account by providing three constraints on the quality and nature of the hypotheses or theories which may be introduced into good scientific practice. These constraints are not always obvious in any narrative account, but they are pervasive enough to provide some sound guidelines for assessing scientific practice. Indeed, they may be so often found in a philosophical analysis of scientific practice that the reasons for their occasional absence may be more interesting than the suggestion that they do not furnish a completely exceptionless methodological account of scientific practice. We may therefore wish to retain them as giving a useful general account, or helping to provide one, even though we can point to some cases which they do not fit. This attitude is not far removed from that which is characteristic of many scientific hypotheses. We describe these constraints as criteria for the viability of a hypothesis: they are the falsifiability criterion, the significance criterion, and the paradigm conservation criterion.

Falsifiability

The *falsifiability criterion* requires of a hypothesis or theory that it be capable of experimental refutation or falsification. This seems a mere slogan, since we can imagine that disagreement might arise in practice as to whether certain views were or were not falsifiable. Many philosophical concepts, such as falsifiability, are often introduced so that it is impossible to tell in practice whether or not something is an instance of one of them. In utilitarian theory for example, that act is defined as right, among various possible acts (usually conceived of as mutually exclusive) in a given situation, which has the best total consequences. Polemically, this is easy to defend, but in practice no one can tell (usually) what the *total consequences* of a given action will be, so utilitarianism does not lead directly to actual choices of action without considerable elaboration. It seems a reasonable restriction on a philosophy of science that it define concepts which can be recognized in scientific practice. Falsifiability can be characterized as susceptibility to adverse data or to adverse theoretical developments.

This abstract notion is somewhat difficult to specify in practice. For should a proposed hypothesis or theory *(mirabile dictu)* be absolutely true, no actual adverse data would ever be encountered save that due to clumsiness or lack of attention. We will regard ourselves as free of this problem by extrapolation from the history of science. A safe course seems to be that of letting the burden of falsifiability lie with the individual proponent of a hypothesis or theory. For a putative hypothesis or theory to be a viable scientific proposal, we require of the proposer that he be able to specify relevant possible experiments and conceivable outcomes of such experiments such that, if these outcomes were obtained, he would take them as serious evidence against his proposal. This falsifiability criterion can still be regarded as incredibly weak, since others may regard a proponent's suggested test as so unlikely to produce counter evidence, or so irrelevant to the content of the proposed hypothesis or theory, that it is worthless. We do not, for example, test cosmological theories by flipping coins. The falsifiability criterion thus exposes a deeper problem of determining what experimental data are relevant to evaluating a given hypothesis.

In developing the falsifiability criterion, it is easy to draw a contrast too sharply between apparently unfalsifiable philosophical or religious theories and scientific theories, attempting to emphasize the connection of the latter with hard data of some kind. But the experiments cited to establish falsifiability in many scientific contexts are only barely conceivable, and not at all practical. In the use of such *gedanken* (thought) experiments, science often seemingly shades off into philosophical speculation of a sort, except for the fact that the theories under discussion in science usually have a relationship to other theories which are in turn relatively firmly tied to certain experimental data. The test of experimental relevance suggested by falsifiability can therefore be recognized in nearly every important theoretical debate in science, but the recognition of detail may require considerable study.

The simple fact is that many statements made by scientists refer to ideal or idealized situations which can at best be reached only by extrapolation from actual data. For example, frictionless surfaces and ideal gases are among the staples of classical physical theorizing, and yet they cannot be studied in the laboratory save indirectly, since no surface is frictionless, and no gas is ideal. Some philosophers have proposed that such ideal cases, being strictly nonexistent, would not appear in a satisfactory philosophical analysis of scientific practice. But this attitude is plainly a mistake. Ideal cases are in many instances the only mathematically tractable examples of theoretical ideas and principles, so that actual cases may be intelligible only when seen as approximations to the ideal cases. The statements about ideal cases are then tested by seeing whether actual cases have properties approaching those of the ideal cases as a series of experiments is performed which approach more and more closely to the theoretically tractable situation.

It has sometimes been objected that this description is not very precise, and cannot be given in terms of precise logical requirements. This is true, but logical requirements have not yet proved very valuable in the analysis of falsifiability. A straightforward logical point might seem to be that a theory is falsified if some experimental datum contradicts some logical consequence of the theory. There is a difficulty here which we have already alluded to. Typically, an actual experimental datum is often not an exact consequence of a theory, which may be about ideal cases. Well, suppose we restrict our attention to a case where some experimental datum does seem to contradict a consequence of a theory. Anyone who reads scientific articles knows that many authors will cite evidence telling against some theory which they nevertheless continue to hold, a situation which seems to violate plain logic. Some of the conservatism expressed in such a situation is due to difficulties with the notion of the relevance of data, a difficulty which has been previously mentioned. It is also true that one may, in the face of counter-evidence, limit the scope of a theory, or modify the theory in some other way while preserving its identity. Often such modifications amount to an outright reinterpretation of the original experiment. For example, some experiments on small particles which seemed to violate certain conservation laws by giving surprising results were reinterpreted by postulating new (and unobserved) particles in order to preserve the laws. If this seems methodologically suspect, that's show business for you. This example is sufficient to indicate one serious flaw in the original description. An experiment set up to test some theory which gives rather unexpected results may issue, not in the selection of the hypothesis which would have been seen as the sole explanation of the data *before* the experiment, but in a revision of the theory, and possibly in a new interpretation of the data after the experiment has been performed.

We have not, so far, attempted to distinguish in scientific practice between *laws, theories,* and *hypotheses.* For the moment, we need no more than the rough and ready distinctions provided in ordinary language. A *law* will be taken as a statement expressing an exact invariance between two or more readily observable experimental properties under relatively well-defined conditions. In classical physics, laws were often discovered by experiment and conjecture, and they were typically named after the individual who made the essential discovery. On the other hand, hypotheses and theories were generally taken to be collections of laws along with other statements of a more general nature which were used to explain a variety of experimental results and observations. It does no harm to think of theories as more comprehensive than hypotheses, except that no particular advantage is obtained. Theories are typically more comprehensive in scope, but comprehensiveness is related to the available data, so that what may be called a theory in one branch of science might seem rather impoverished by comparison to a theory which explains a comparatively broad range of experimental data in some other branch. Because of this relativity to data, there seems little point in attempting an absolute characterization of these terms. One may, for example, compare the theory of evolution with the special theory of relativity. The latter has many direct experimentally describable consequences for particular physical systems, while the former says very little about particular biological systems unless it is supplemented with particular hypotheses about adaptation, selection pressure, and so on. After we have discussed scientific practice in more detail, we will return to a much closer discussion of what a theory is, and the role that it plays in sound scientific practice. For the moment, we will take theories as the most general kinds of statements advanced by scientists to explain and to integrate a batch of experimental data.

The difficulties with attempting to state a precise criterion of falsifiability are symptomatic of those encountered in pursuing analysis of scientific practice. We start by agreeing that a scientific statement should be testable by experiment, and testable in the strong sense that situations can be described in which it would be rejected. Then we have the difficulties that ideal cases are rather circuitously related to actual experiment, and the fact that apparent outright counter-evidence may be rationally dismissed in some instances. It becomes increasingly clear that falsifiability is somehow involved, but not very clear how it is involved in a general characterization of scientific practice. A good suspicion is that the falsifiability criterion is stronger in practice than it is in theory. Any scientist who cannot specify falsifying circumstances for a statement which seems relevant to the sustained scrutiny of his peers, or who defends a statement in terms of what his peers generally regard as ad hoc adjustments, is probably violating the falsifiability requirement. The idea here is that relevance, like proof, is something which can usually be demonstrated by sufficient attention to the detailed facts of the situation. We will therefore assume that familiarity with the area of science in which a theory is advanced will enable one to make a decision as to whether the falsifiability criterion has been adequately met and we will also assume that it is proper to ask of a theory what kind of test its advocates could specify which might plausibly result in data which could cause one to reject it.

Significance

Good scientists loathe unassimilated information. Sometimes a scientist may do something just to see what will happen, but when it does, a poor theoretical explanation is preferred to none at all. We can use this fact to find a rational basis for a scientist's reluctance to give up received theories in the face of experimental counter-evidence in some situations. Because it probably does not make sense to say that *science* accepts such and such a theory at a given time, we will continue to relativize our problem to an individual scientist confronted with some as yet unassimilated data. A scientist does not start just with this data, for he will also hold various beliefs (such that certain laws, hypotheses, or theories are correct) in the light of past experience or instruction. To be viable, a new proposal must explain the significance of some of the data which cannot be explained, or can be only poorly explained, by beliefs already accepted by the scientist and his peers. The proposer must show that his theory can provide a better explanation of at least some of the data than any other known proposal. A viable new proposal need not explain all of the past data in the relevant area to satisfy the proposed criterion, but it must explain some reasonable range of data better than any rival. The significance criterion is designed to block redundant hypotheses within the limits of experimental error, while insuring that all of the data be covered by some explanatory hypothesis, law, or theory.

The significance criterion is more important than the logical requirement of consistency, namely, that a scientist will not entertain mutually inconsistent scientific hypotheses. A history of the wave-particle hypotheses about the nature of light transmission is a useful case in point. As usually expressed, these hypotheses are logically inconsistent. Data about light transmission were gradually accumulated that could only be explained by a kind of theoretical schizophrenia. Interference phenomenon seemed best explained by the hypothesis that light signals were a wave phenomenon, and the photo-electric effect best explained by the hypothesis that light signals are beams of particles. In classical physics, however, waves and particles have contradictory properties. In the face of this fact, most scientists (and some very good ones by common consent) used *both* hypotheses, choosing that one in any particular situation which seemed to have the best explanatory power. The logical inconsistency apparently involved in this practice could be technically removed by associating only one of the hypotheses with each experimental situation. But this is false to practice, since scientists were quite willing to note that some data were explained equally well by both hypotheses, and no sharp division of practice in these cases seemed desirable as a means of keeping a technical consistency.*

It is not that consistency is not desired. The point is that conflicting theories are sometimes jointly used to provide explanations of the total range of data, with the hope that some means of reinterpreting the hypotheses might be discovered which would remove the inconsistency. Finding some explanation or account of each batch of data may thus override consistency during the growth of scientific practice. The history of science provides many cases of the joint use of conflicting hypotheses where each is superior to the other in explaining some of the data. A complete theory for some wide range of data should be consistent, but such theories are the exception. In general, significance is more important than consistency. A scientist seems to prefer some explanation of all of the data, even though the theories involved may clash, to a situation in which some of the data is explained by a logically consistent set of hypotheses, while the rest of the data is simply unexplained.

In the face of new data which conflicts with accepted theory, the falsifiability and significance criteria by themselves allow a wide range of choice in making theoretical proposals and in judging their viability.

Paradigm Conservation

Our last criterion, *paradigm conservation,* places a much more severe restriction on the viability of theories, hypotheses, and laws. Clearly, if data is unassimilated, we can suppose that it is not very well explained within the conceptual framework of any existing theories. In spite of the change and development of theories in the face of new data, however, there seems to

---

*See the books by N. R. Hanson cited in the Bibliography for a detailed discussion.

be a conservative constraint on the outlines of new theoretical developments imposed by a relatively small number of physical and mathematical ideas which seem to occur throughout the history of science. Atomic and field theories, action by contact and action at a distance, particulate and wave transmission of energy, and so forth, provide an existing stock of contrasting ideas embodied in tractable mathematical models which the theorist is nearly certain to survey in constructing new proposals. It is a reasonable feeling that the number of such paradigm ideas is not enormous, even though the variety of their applications is. Confronted with anomalous data, and offered the choice between a new formalism describing the data in terms of a generalization or application of a wave transmission of some kind of energy or a new formalism provided with no interpretation that does however fit the data closely, a scientist might be expected to choose the former. This conservatism seems justifiable, since the revised paradigm has already proven useful. Conservatism here is a criterion for the viability of theoretical scientific proposals, suggesting that maintenance of a past model is to be preferred over a completely new model, even at the expense of some closer fit to the data.

The criterion of paradigm conservation does not prevent the introduction of completely new models and completely new ideas. It does suggest that these are not viable and will not play an important role in scientific practice unless reliable data is found (results accepted by critics after their own trials) which is simply not explicable by a hypothesis, law, or theory embodying existing ideas. Paradigm conservation also suggests that scientific revolutions are less frequent than some historians have mentioned.

The criterion of paradigm conservation, introduced as a filter against crackpot proposals, is not compatible with the idea that a single theory must triumph over its rivals as data is accumulated. Different scientists may accept different paradigms as starting points because of training or other factors, and the criterion allows simultaneous development and conflict between rival paradigm ideas in proposed new explanations for unassimilated data. At any given time, therefore, conflicting explanations of the same data may be offered on the basis of paradigm conservation. Historians looking at these conflicting explanations are likely to emphasize that the relationship between theory, law, or hypothesis and the data to be accounted for is different in different paradigms. For some paradigms, the elements or basic structures of the mathematical models (or other expressions of the paradigm) are subject to direct inspection of some kind, and in other cases not. It appears, therefore, that even the criterion of paradigm conservation is quite permissive.

What are we to make of our three criteria? There is, unfortunately, no easy answer as to how to take them all together in particular cases. This situation is not very novel, and less troublesome than it may seem at first. Major league baseball scouts, for example, want to find ball players who can hit, run, catch, and throw. Other things being equal, the idea is to maximize each of these attributes. Yet there are few ideal ball players. The weighting of various factors in actual cases depends upon who is available, what positions need to be filled, and so forth, and occasionally the normal criteria are forgotten for the kind of player who can have an exceptional influence on his teammates. If we look at the difficulties involved, we might conclude that sound assessment of baseball players is impossible, which is clearly absurd. In common practice, the scientist will usually be sensitive to the criterion of falsifiability for every available theory, and the available theories are likely to be largely determined by paradigm conservation. This means that significance can be terribly important, but may not lead to an unequivocal decision. One may have to decide on the merits of each case whether theory A explains some data so much better than theory B that it should be accepted, even though theory B has good credentials in terms of paradigm conservation.

Philosophically reconstructed history of science does not lead directly from these criteria to an interesting general philosophy of science, incorporating an account of general scientific methodology that has bite in terms of particular examples from practice. The upshot of the philosophical re-construction is rather a batch of historical cases, and analyses of these cases, which one may or may not be able to use in evaluating a new theoretical proposal, and which one may or may not be able to use in singling out a best move in some historical scientific controversy. As with most history, the emphasis is on the insight that can be brought to historical problems in the light of that outcome, and not on finding laws that will enable us to project the future. The criteria may enable us to see with hindsight that certain obstructive positions taken by certain scientists could have been avoided, but they do not enable us to see, except darkly, into present scientific controversy.

3

The Logic of Science

The methods of historical inquiry are not likely to produce a lot of false statements about the development of scientific practice. By resisting generalization, and relying on cases, the philosophical historian can produce persuasive evidence that a general explanatory account of the structure of scientific practice is impossible. Many philosophers of science have therefore rejected the rather obvious starting point of scientific history, and they have proposed other lines for developing a sound technical philosophy of science.

Suppose we approach a new theoretical proposal from the viewpoint suggested in the last chapter. In order to assess the proposal in terms of the criterion of paradigm conservation, some close study of the existing paradigms and the past history of the relevant scientific practice are required. This close study is what seems to limit the philosopher from making very wide-ranging assessments, since there are obvious limitations on the history of scientific practice which can be mastered by a single individual. These limitations may be real, but they do not themselves preclude the development of another approach.

Most of the approaches to the philosophy of science which

have rejected historical methodology as a starting point have been conceived as an application of the scientific method (rather than historical method) to the study of scientific practice. A feature of scientific method on any reasonably general description is the pervasive development of highly abstract models in a suitable symbolism which are initially proposed to fit conceptually simplified cases, and which are then gradually made more sophisticated by relaxing constraints to obtain more general models until a comprehensive scope of explanation of data is finally obtained. Philosophy of science can be thought of on these grounds as a series of theories about theories. The strategy is persuasive. A sound technical language and symbolism exist in the form of the logical systems and the study of axiomatics which have been developed by contemporary formal logicians. Simple models of laws, theories, and hypotheses are then constructed in terms of these logical systems to account for the structure of scientific practice, and the models can be made increasingly sophisticated while retaining logical precision in the face of any adverse evidence. The prospect of a series of increasingly sophisticated logical models suggests that perhaps the philosophy of science can be regarded as a cumulative body of knowledge not dissimilar in its dynamics of development from science itself.

In attempting to apply scientific methodology to the study of science, one can justify rather severe abstraction by appeal to various abstractive techniques in science. One kind of abstraction has been to restrict the study of scientific practice to an analysis of its structure at some time, rather than attempting the analysis of a development over time directly. In biology, for example, a developing animal may be studied (and often is) by looking at temporal slices of its structure. Taking a temporal slice for empirical study often requires the death or alteration of the particular animal used as a specimen. The technique of studying temporal slices works only if enough theoretically equivalent animals can be furnished to provide the temporal slices.

An historian may argue that the technique of taking temporal slices must fail in analyzing the development of science because suitably equivalent theoretical developments are not sufficiently common in scientific history. But we should be willing to give the logician his chance. If the assumption that common logical models are possible for any sound development is correct, then a study of suitable temporal slices of various developments should exhibit the features of these models under analysis.

The study of a logical structure between a theory, law, or hypothesis and the data at a given time is often called by technical philosophers the study of the *context of justification.* It is argued that the origins of a theory, law, or hypothesis can be ignored in such a study, and the relationship of a single theory (let us say) to data can be studied in abstraction from the relationships of other theories to the same data. As a result of a great deal of argument in the past twenty years, it now seems clear that the idea of the context of justification as a useful abstraction is closely tied to the conception that the truth of data reports is independent of the significance of the theories which are to be related to them. The historians have consistently challenged this. According to the historians, the data have been accumulated because of the theories available for test, and the data are given significance only when seen as instances of the tested theories. Consequently, data cannot be taken to have significance in a temporal slice independently of the entire range of possible theories which are viable at that time. The rejoinder is that scientists usually do so evaluate data without knowing the entire range of theoretical proposals, so that a model for evaluation cannot require this extensive knowledge. We will again take the position that it is reasonable to see what can be developed on the basis of the assumption that abstraction to the context of justification is legitimate.

Philosophers of science who construct logical models usually regard themselves as engaged in a cooperative comprehensive program along with scientists. Scientists collect the facts and the theories, and the philosophers examine their structure and their relationships. Instead of striking a reflective attitude in intellectual examination of scientific practice, these philosophers suggest that they roll up their sleeves and get to work. The appeal of this suggestion lies in the fact that symbolic logic shades off into mathematics, so that the role of the philosopher as logical analyst has an apparent analogy to the role of the pure mathematician as scientific advisor. (The mathematician, of course, has other roles.) The philosopher is supposed to be able to determine whether, for example, a given theory really explains given data if the scientist should care to ask him.

Using the technical equipment of logic, it is possible to find a great many puzzles in the characterization of methodology provided in the simple description of the last chapter. Contrary to historical studies which suggest that scientists have had difficulty in inventing new hypotheses to fit available data, the logician is fond of pointing out that an infinite number of hypotheses can always be fitted to any available data. Logic thus turns the problem on its head. The problem is not to find hypotheses; it is that there is a potential embarrassment of riches. Criteria of significance and of paradigm conservation are relevant to this problem in an historical context, but in a context of justification, we need to find a property of a theory, law, or hypothesis not dependent either upon the existing alternatives or the historical development which will rule out the unwanted but logically possible proposals. The major suggestion that has been proposed is that this can be accomplished by means of assigning to a viable theory, law, or hypothesis a formal *simplicity index*. We would then have the following situation.

A given theory (let us say for convenience) will either explain the data we are concerned with, or it will not. Again, it may or may not also be regarded as confirmed by these data. The relationships of explanation and confirmation involved are supposed to be given a precise characterization in terms of logical models. For simplicity of exposition, suppose we have several theories proposed which are confirmed by, but do not explain, the relevant data. Those theories are then viable among these which share the lowest simplicity index, where the *lowest* index is chosen conventionally to insure that lower indices are correlated with intuitively simpler theories. In the ideal case, this requirement would single out a single theory as the simplest, and hence the only viable alternative. The problem of finding a suitable formal criterion of simplicity is representative of the kind of research problem suggested by the use of logical models of scientific practice.

Technical philosophy of science has usually treated theories, laws, and hypotheses as instances of axiomatic systems. In a given temporal slice of the development of science, a theory, law, or hypothesis is a statement or set of statements along with all of the logical consequences of that statement or set of statements. For the analysis of significance, it is required that these statements be expressed in terms of a formal axiomatic system satisfying certain requirements. In such treatments, the intuitive distinctions between theories, laws, and hypotheses tend to disappear, but it is suggested that they may be preserved by requirements on the kinds of symbols and logical forms used in the axiomatization.

In order to have an example specific enough to give some impression of the proposed logical models, we will consider the proposed logical models and also the proposed constant correlation (or invariance) between two properties of possible objects of observation expressed by the statement "All ravens are black." This statement has in fact been often discussed by philosophers of science as a statement exhibiting the important formal feature of a scientific law. In these terms, a law always states that all objects of a certain kind are objects of another kind; or equivalently, that no object has a certain property while failing to have another specified property. It has already been suggested that the relationships of explanation and confirmation between a law and data are important for logical models of scientific practice. The analyses of explanation and confirmation which have been proposed in logical models depend heavily on the notion of deductive consequence familiar from the development of logical systems.

We can start with explanation. In a scientific context, it seems reasonable to require that if some datum does not follow from a theory, that theory cannot explain the datum.

To say that the general theory of relativity explains the trajectory of rays of light from the sun to the earth is apparently to say that these trajectories are a consequence of the general theory. But the general theory does not talk about the earth and the sun. An explanation is obtained when particular information about the earth and the sun as observed objects is substituted into the equations of the theory with the consequence that trajectories can be deduced which are those actually observed. One can only regret the oversimplifications involved in such a short description, but something like this *general* pattern is common to a great many of the actual explanations offered in science. We will say that in a logical model one statement is explained by a law if it can be deduced from that law when certain information is provided giving the circumstances of application in which we are interested. This general conception is known as the deductive model of scientific explanation. The role of the logic is to insure that the statement explained is a logical consequence of the law (or theory) doing the explaining in conjunction with certain other information. In terms of our example, someone could be able to explain why an object, say object number 1214 in a catalog of stuffed ornithological specimens, was black, by relying on the fact expressed in the catalog that number 1214 is a raven, and the proposed law under consideration. This example is trivial, but it can be said to illustrate the logical structure of explanation in the same sense that the banal quarrels of logic texts can be said to illustrate the logical structure of sound argument.

This simple idea is not easily extended into a formal logical model. To begin with, the appropriate logical system for expressing the relationship of *following from* used in the intuitive account is a matter of some controversy. Further, even if the deductive pattern can be made clear, it seems that this kind of pattern is only one kind of explanation used in the sciences, and it would need to be supplemented by other models in any very comprehensive general logical model for the structure of contexts of justification to be assessed against a wide range of scientific practice.

We will now look briefly at confirmation. A logical model usually holds that a law is *confirmed* by data if the data are consistent with every appropriate logical consequence of the law. More enigmatically but correctly, we may say that a law is confirmed by given data if the law would not be false if the data represented our total factual knowledge of the universe. We can examine what this would mean for "All ravens are black." To do this, it is convenient to suppose that the data to be considered can be represented by names of observed objects placed on the following grid:

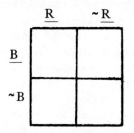

A particular datum would be expressed by the appearance of a unique name for the observed object placed in one of the four squares depending on whether it is a raven or not, and whether it is black or not. This supposition expresses a rather strong position about the nature of data, for it is possible to think of things for which names would not fit easily into the grid but which might be described in possible data for some laws or theories. For example, the observed kinetic energy of a falling particle will have to go into the lower right-hand corner of this grid if we consider it as an observed datum, but it does not do so very comfortably.

Our example also embodies a strong presupposition about observation. We may not be able to observe the exact length of a rod because of errors in measurement, but we must suppose that ravens and black objects are subject to sharp discrimination, so that each datum fits clearly into one of the four squares. Let us suppose that by an appropriate abstraction, we can consider the metaphysics explained and the observations made appropriately. The proposed law "All ravens are black" says that the lower left-hand square of the grid is empty, as it is equivalent to the statement "There is no non-black raven." We may then say that the data confirm the proposed law if there are data in the grid, and if no datum has been placed in the lower left-hand corner of the grid.

The objections to these simple logical models of explanation and confirmation are quite serious, and they are a consequence of the admittedly severe abstraction from actual scientific practice which underlies them. Of the two models, the one for explanation seems satisfactory in a wider range of cases. Although actual scientific explanation is rarely explicitly deductive in the logician's sense, most scientists would consider it a defect in an actual scientific explanation if it could be shown that the theories and facts alluded to could be true while the explained statement (or explained event expressed in a statement) was false, that is, if the explained statement could be shown not to follow from the theories and facts alluded to. It is not an objection to this that some everyday explanations and working scientific explanations which are accepted as useful cannot be shown to have the appropriate deductive structure utilizing laws or theories. Not all explanation is scientific explanation in the sense of the logical model, but we can reasonably take some requirement of deductivity as a necessary condition in much of idealized scientific explanation.

The really problematic difficulties with the deductive model came not from the general conception of explanation which it offers, but from technical defects in every known careful formulation of the model. Either the models permit the construction of explanations satisfying their conditions which are plainly of no scientific merit, or they become too restrictive in the course of ruling out these counter-intuitive cases. The details can be pursued in the literature. On the whole, however, the usefulness of the deductive model of explanation may yet be established in some measure of generality.

A direct attack on the deductive model is sometimes made by citing laws or theories containing probabilities, and arguing that there is a sense of explanation involving such laws or theories in which the statement explained does not follow deductively from the laws or theories involved. This attack, if successful, means that the deductive account of explanation must be supplemented by at least one additional model for a kind of statistical explanation. From laws or theories containing probability statements, we can often deduce other probability statements. Strictly, no data can ever prove such a probability statement false by logical inference. This fact, and the fact that nearly all measurement involves probability theory in the assessment of error, has led some philosophers to the plainly incorrect view that laws and theories are never disproved. To eradicate this view, it is enough to look into old textbooks and find proposed laws and theories which would be regarded now as false, or at least wrong.

Our falsifiability criterion was designed to take this into account, requiring the holder of a law or theory incorporating probability statements to specify the kind of data that would lead him, in the absence of new countervailing information, to abandon or modify his original proposals. Now as to general laws or theories, a law or theory involving probabilities cannot explain anything unless more specific information is supplied, and this will often be in the form of a probability statement about particular individuals. I think that fixed observational data cannot be explained by laws or theories so augmented, and such data can only confirm a theory, doing so if its calculated parameters (statistics) are sufficiently close to the parameters elicited from the law or theory when additional information is provided. Laws or theories, however, will explain idealized probability statements which sufficient data may force us to accept as true. Genetic theory, for example, will explain why three-fourths of all of the offspring of certain parental stock will display a certain property, even though three-fourths of the offspring are not found to display this property in any particular experiment. The experiments, however, may give us reason to accept this percentage, and then an explanation is forthcoming. It is not clear whether the widespread use of probability statements in science requires the adoption of another notion of explanation.

A more serious challenge to the deductive model is raised where there seems to be knowledge or understanding of how particular events have come about in the absence of any general laws and theories from which they may be deduced, even with supplementation by appropriate fact. We sometimes understand, for example, why a human being does something, even though we have no general laws or theories about human behavior. The absence of general laws and theories becomes more pronounced as we move from physics to biology, biology to psychology, and from psychology to sociology. In a later chapter, we will see why this may be so in a fashion which does not depend upon the widening use of statistical generalizations as one moves through the same sequence. Provided that we do not make the possession of knowledge equivalent to the ability to provide deductive explanations in terms of laws and theories, this is no embarrassment. There is knowledge and understanding independently of deductive explanations. Whether supplementary notions of explanation are required for the analysis of such knowledge and understanding, and how it is to be related to scientific knowledge in general on logical models, is at present a moot point. Philosophical analysis has not dealt extensively with cases other than those of physics where deductive explanation undoubtedly does play an important role.

We turn now to the notion of confirmation embedded in the logical models. Let us return to our grid. Suppose we observe a batch of ravens which are black. This would seem intuitively to confirm (in the technical sense) the statement "All ravens are black." Now hang on to your hat! The proposed law says merely that the lower left-hand corner of the grid is empty. Therefore, every object which we can place in the grid in some square other than the lower left-hand one would seem equally to confirm the statement. I observe a white hankerchief. This observation is compatible with the claim that none of the objects in the world belong in the lower left-hand corner, so it seems to confirm (technically) the statement "All ravens are black" as well as does the observation of a black raven so long as we keep to the technical criterion of confirmation in the model. The tangle that results from our supposing that an observation of a white handkerchief could tell us something about birds is known in the literature as the *paradox of confirmation.* It is a good example of the problems that beset the construction of logical models in the philosophy of science: it's intellectually interesting, but it has no direct consequences for scientific practice since we can recognize immediately that something is wrong.

The sources of the problem could reside in a number of points. For one thing, the grid representation of a law is taken from the standard logical analysis of the structure of law statements, but this analysis may be wrong. We will not pursue this possibility here, since no alternative construal of the structure of law statements is available which does not encounter equally serious difficulties. Instead, we will concentrate on the answer of some logicians who feel that the model can be retained by simply rejecting the paradox as a confusion based on a misleading intuition. This defense is supported by carefully drawing attention to the nature of the abstraction which gives rise to the paradox. From this point of view, we can hold that if we had made no prior observations of the world and we were attempting to confirm the proposed law from scratch, an early observation of a white handkerchief *would* confirm the statement about the ravens. This has the virtue of clarity and directness, but it is surely eccentric in spirit.

Now on the one hand, it is all right to discuss hypothetical universes which, say, have only two particles in them by way of abstracting from the complexities of the real world for scientific purposes. In these cases, we can experiment on a series of two-particle systems which are progressively decoupled from the rest of the world to get a line on what would happen in a universe in which there were only two particles. If, on the other hand, we discuss a human being who is said to know only that one or two statements are true, what are we to make of this situation? We cannot test it sensibly by imagining a man (or a scientist) so intellectually impoverished as to have this as his only information. The reply leaves no doubt that this is a foundational effort which is part of an attempt to build up a satisfactory general theory of confirmation so that when the information is added that there are far fewer ravens than non-ravens (which we undoubtedly assumed in the original case), we can draw the conclusion that a white handkerchief is not a confirming instance of "All ravens are black."

We can give foundational studies any answer they require for circumscribed problems. Our interest in them for the philosophy of science must ultimately hinge on whether they can provide a general theory of confirmation which will explain the decisions encountered in sound scientific practice. The plain fact is that there is no theory of confirmation or support based solely on logical relationships provided by an extant logical model which in any way seems capable of fitting a wide range of good scientific practice.

There are two proposals for avoiding the difficulties associated with confirmation theory. One is to attempt utilization of probability notions, and the other is to abandon any suggestion that confirmation is a notion which should be used to analyze scientific practice.

The latter suggestion has some plausibility when it is compared to practice. Explanation plays a self-conscious role in scientific practice that confirmation does not. Scientists are not interested in simply piling up confirming instances for a law or theory. Endless experimental tests of well-known laws by students in school are not taken seriously as adding to the sum of scientific knowledge. In spite of this, any widely discussed scientific theory cannot depend for viability on the mere absence of counter-examples to it. As was suggested by the criterion of significance in the last chapter, a viable theory must explain some data or expected data not explained, or explained very poorly, by its extant theoretical rivals. Perhaps confirmation has this character—that it consists of data compatible only with one theory or law in a given area, singling it out as the extant theory most likely to be correct. Confirmation of a theory thus occurs by given data only when the data are most likely on that theory by comparison to their rivals. If this is so, we can retain the idea that confirmation or experimental support is a useful notion, even though the best confirmed theory may be rejected in favor of another because of considerations of paradigm conservation. The failure of the logical models to provide a suitable characterization of confirmation is then pinpointed in their supposition that confirmation is a relation between a single theory and a fixed set of data, rather than being a relation between a set of alternative theories, one of these theories, and data.

To say this is to drift toward the supposition that probability models may be required to explain some useful notion of confirmation. I think that this is basically correct. There are models for confirmation inferences based on Bayes' Theorem in which one law or theory from a suitable range may be singled out by given data as most likely (or as likely as any), and these models are used in actual scientific practice. In the relevant context, Bayes' Theorem says that the probability of a theory or hypothesis after an experiment is the product of its probability prior to the experiment and the likelihood of getting the experimental data given the truth of the hypothesis. It follows from this that if some experimental data are about equally likely no matter whether theory A or theory B is true, then the experiment does not change our estimate of the two theories. This is clearly related to paradigm conservation. Similarly, if two theories A and B seem equally probable before an experiment, and the experimental data are much more likely given that theory A is true than if theory B is true, we often accept theory A and reject theory B as a result of the experiment. This, in turn, is clearly related to the significance criterion. More complicated analyses of experimental data require a look at the mathematical theory.* Inference based on Bayes' Theorem has not been widely accepted by philosophers of science, possibly due to problems with assigning probabilities directly to theories or laws. Such assignments require the use of subjective or a priori logical probabilities. Programs for assigning a priori logical probabilities exist, but so far they are of very limited

---

*For an elementary introduction, see Robert Ackermann, *Nondeductive Inference* (Routledge, London, 1966).

scope, and they entail some clearly counter-intuitive claims. Subjective probabilities have been ruled out by many philosophers of science because they seem to be non-objective in view of the fact that they cannot be empirically determined. These methods have consequently won only minority allegiance, but it may well be that a solution to the extant problems of confirmation must lie in invoking one of these notions of probability in conjunction with Bayes' Theorem.

The logical models of science that have here been mentioned are at most about thirty years old. Whether their defects and difficulties stem from a wrong method of studying scientific practice, or whether they will be overcome by more sophisticated models in the future is a matter of fierce debate, with some good points to be scored for both sides. We will therefore not attempt any overall assessment, which would be unfair anyway in view of the simplified nature of our presentation of the relevant views. From a larger perspective, however, it is quite clear that even if the logical models were to be more satisfactorily constructed, many significant problems about the development of scientific practice would elude those logical models based solely on the context of justification. We still have some unexplored problems concerning the development of scientific practice which are worth discussion.

4

The Evolution of Science

Historical and logical methodologies have dominated recent attempts to analyze scientific practice with a view to finding a philosophically coherent account which will provide an explanation of the significant features of sound or fruitful practice. It seems legitimate to claim that neither of these approaches has as yet produced a general account that matches the desiderata of a broad philosophical program of analysis. On the one hand, historical studies have often illuminated particular segments of scientific history, but it is not clear that their results have any explanatory value in assessing current practice, other than the profit which may accrue when some study of the past provides a significant insight for an individual engaged in some problem of his own. The historical studies, considered as a whole, do not offer much encouragement for the view that a general philosophy of science with valuable explanatory principles is possible. Philosophical historians have suggested rather that general methodology is only a vague heuristic, and the real philosophical problems in science can arise only for those scientists sufficiently familiar with live theoretical debate to take an active part in it. On the other hand, no one can say that the logical models are not general, or that they are not precise.

The problem is rather that their criteria are entirely destructive of actual practice, making even paradigm achievements of scientific genius to be but confused gropings for the features of some austere logical machinery. Logical models now proposed in the literature seem hopelessly restricted and inadequate as they now stand, since they illuminate and explain only a small segment of the wide range of actual instances of intuitively sound scientific practice. But even if revised models attain interesting scope without sacrifice of precision, it is fairly clear that they could supply solutions to only some of the questions that we would like to ask about the development of scientific practice. Even if developed theories can be represented as axiomatic systems within a context of justification, the logical models constructed on this basis would not answer crucial questions about the course of development of new theories.

There are two notions which philosophy of science has often used somewhat uncritically, and these notions underly implicit philosophical views which may well be responsible for the impasse between historical and logical analyses of scientific practice. The notions are *rationality* and *objectivity*, and in this chapter I shall discuss some ideas related to these notions which will permit us to draw a philosophically more coherent view of a wide range of intuitively sound practice.

In the past, rationality has been ascribed by philosophers to human beings whose beliefs are characterized by logical consistency and a very careful comparison of theoretical proposals to available fact. A classic formulation is that the strength of a belief should be proportional to the available evidence for that belief in a rational individual. For this purpose, proposed theories, laws, and hypotheses can all be regarded as possible scientific beliefs of an individual. This characteristic must furthermore not be accidental, in the sense that the rational man should achieve proportionate belief by calculation and reflection, and not by accident. Accidental rationality, so to speak, is so intuitively improbable that we will ignore the whole problem of how a man could come to be in the state characterizing rationality, and simply examine the state. Since the state characterizes the strength of belief in a given statement solely as a function of available evidence, this description of rationality can be described as severely empirical.

At any time in the history of science the same evidence is potentially available to all scientists, so it would seem that insofar as scientists approach rationality and assimilate this body of evidence, they would tend to have the same belief structures. The appeal of this formulation is that on it supposedly crazy beliefs—Communist agents are responsible for the fluoridation of our water, a first step in their takeover plan—would have very little evidence in their support, so that a rational man would slough off such beliefs along with various hastily considered judgments. This is in fact a far from easy model to defend in detail because of the way in which holders of crazy beliefs evaluate the data that seem obvious to the sane. Experience with the holders of crazy beliefs is sufficient to establish that crazy beliefs are often compatible with (technically *confirmed* by) an amazing mass of evidence.

A deranged man who believes (falsely) that his brother is attempting to kill him may interpret the same actions which others see as establishing the brother's good intentions as an attempt by the brother to pretend goodwill in order to establish a sound court case after he is found dead. Abnormal psychology texts can furnish truly amazing accounts of the assimilation of data by lunatic beliefs. The behavior of some scientists has shown an uncomfortable formal similarity to this syndrome. To rule this out while maintaining that a severely empirical characterization should be retained for rationality, it is necessary to force evidence and beliefs into logical systems satisfying various stringent formal requirements, but it has not been possible so far to find a completely satisfactory formal characterization of rationality even when such formalization is undertaken.

To see what may be misleading in the traditional account

of rationality applied to a scientific setting, we can look briefly at its consequences for the history of science. Using it as a guide, we would expect a rational scientist to be interested primarily in the accumulation of data, changing his belief structure so as to keep a rational relationship between it and the available evidence. If this view were correct, idealized scientific history would be rather peaceful, and historians would properly lament the actual argumentation of scientists as a lapse from ideal rationality. This view is topsy-turvy. If we take scientific progress as a paradigm of rationality, we ought to expect to define rationality in terms of the pervasive features of the paradigm datum, and historical studies seem to indicate that argumentation is of the substance of scientific progress. Rationality *in science* cannot therefore be suitably represented in a temporal slice of the development of scientific practice. To put it succinctly, while rationality may be captured conveniently by the notion of consistency (which can be represented in a temporal slice) in the development of mathematical or philosophical knowledge, rationality in science is to be characterized as the way in which beliefs change with increasing evidence over a temporal period. The reason for this probably lies in the fact that the objects of mathematical investigation and of traditional philosophical analysis were unchanging, or so slowly changing that process could be conveniently ignored. But the progress of science depends on new data and novel situations which are provided by changing techniques of investigation. A scientist confronted with *novel* data is free to choose his beliefs and to introduce new ideas subject only to the modest constraints imposed by the criteria of falsifiability, significance, and paradigm conservation.

What distinguishes the rational from the irrational scientist is not the exact character of the new proposals he may accept in the fact of novel data, but rather the way in which these beliefs are modified in the light of accumulating evidence. A belief structure, that in some sense changes not at all or changes too slowly in the face of accumulating counter-evidence, can be considered scientifically irrational. This perspective on rationality has an empirical base, but it is not severely empirical. The Rationality becomes measured by response to new evidence, but the initial beliefs of a scientist are a matter of wide latitude in choice and their initial strengths are not determined by the evidence. In this way, rationality leaves scope for personal judgment or hunch without being divorced from objective criteria for assessing beliefs over a period of time. The implicit assumptions of recent empiricism suggest that this view of rationality is too loose, but I think that it must be adopted eventually by philosophers of science in view of the following consideration.

Our example for the logical model of confirmation ("All ravens are black") was such that both of the properties mentioned in the proposed law could be directly observed. Theories, on the other hand, often contain mention of the properties of some individuals whose existence is postulated to provide a coherent explanation of various phenomena, but which are so small or so far away, or whatever, that they cannot be directly observed by current techniques of observation or measurement. Scientific theories cannot therefore be seen as abstractions from the available evidence, but are often free constructions of human intelligence which are as creative as any human activity could be. Rationality is not in question when a theoretical proposal is made (provided only that the loose constraints are satisfied), but rationality is in question in science after the proposal has been offered to other scientists for consideration. The facts surrounding the proposal of new theories thus seem to preclude any severely empirical account of scientific progress. The problem is to see how this conclusion can be accepted without losing control of the development of science in terms of an appropriate philosophical analysis.

A clue to the solution is to be found in the connection of rationality with objectivity. Objectivity has been defined in the past in terms of freedom from personal bias, or in terms of a relationship between belief and a fixed external reality. The idea that there is a fixed external reality which presents itself in perception leads severely empiricist philosophies to suppose that data statements can embody information which we *know* to be true of this external reality. On this view, the objectivity of science is explained by the objective character of data statements, and any scientist can discover the truth of these statements by bringing himself into the appropriate circumstances. The data statements are thus the ultimate and unyielding check on the development of scientific theory. Whether the agreement provided by this check is explained by a causal theory of perception plus the postulated nature of the external reality, or whether it is explained by overwhelming majority agreement, the position which it outlines seems philosophically suspect and incompatible with scientific history.

The philosophical difficulties are raised by versions of the mind-body problem, that is, in any attempt to explain how mental or brain events can be known to be suitably similar to properties of the external world. This problem in this context obviously cannot be solved, and it is clearly a consequence of a mistaken approach to the objectivity of data. The properties which most observers might well agree about —say simple colors—are clearly *not* the properties involved in most crucial data statements in scientific practice. Scientific observation is typically *trained* observation: a scientist must learn how to observe data. In a scientific observation, an object is often seen as though it were an instance of some ideal case discussed in a theoretical proposal, and the roughness of the given phenomenological data is largely ignored.

The psychological evidence seems firmly in support of the contention that observation is never free from presupposition in the sense that we can only see what we are prepared to believe that we may see. Put bluntly, the point may seem to entail the view that we can never see anything completely novel and, in a sense, this is precisely correct. We may see the unusual or the unexpected, but when we can we can also nearly always describe what it is that we have seen in some fashion, although not necessarily in any great detail. Again, we often see just what we expect to see, even though what we look at is later found to be something else.

Observation, particularly the important case of visually seeing things, is conditioned by our evolutionary development and by our accepted beliefs. A brute and troublesome consequence of this position is that it may appear to deny completely the independence of data and belief, so that a scientific observer need never give up a belief since he will observe only data which conform to that belief. If we admit personal bias in every observation on the grounds that an individual's belief determine his observations and if we accept the historical point that near unanimity of opinion (even about observation) has often proved wrong in retrospect, we may seem to be in the position of making science completely subjective. If belief conditions observation, why should beliefs ever change on the basis of contravening data?

What seems curiously missing from the philosophical argumentation about this point is the recognition that the same person can examine several different and conflicting beliefs at the same time, or at least over a period of time. Philosophers have often supposed that a scientist will accept just one of a set of conflicting beliefs on the basis of data, and should this be correct, it is difficult to see how that belief would have to be changed. But we have said that the way in which beliefs change is constitutive of rationality. And we can't have it that a scientist simply examines all possible beliefs all of the time against evidential reports, since this is contrary to the obvious advocacy of specific beliefs by individual scientists.

There are at least two particular cases to be discussed. One is the case where a particular observation seems anomalous or puzzling; we then find a belief which explains it and renders it non-puzzling. The other is the common case where we make a series of observations, and then discuss which beliefs may best account for these observations. If belief conditions observation, how can an observation be made of an anomalous datum not explicable in terms of some currently held belief?

There is no easy answer to these questions, but I believe that the hunt for an answer takes one necessarily into murky areas of speculation about brain mechanisms which few empiricist philosophers have been willing to chart out. To begin with, the evolutionary development of man has doubtless provided man with brain mechanisms some of whose operations can be philosophically articulated as the fitting of certain beliefs to sensory inputs. The simple fact here is that sensory input not having certain temporal and spatial qualities will be suppressed as deviant, and the rest will be taken or analyzed into objects worthy of closer scrutiny. By this means, an unarticulated belief that something is there can arise from sensory input, and lead to much closer scrutiny. Other mechanisms can then be brought into play to effect further structuring of the sensory input, some of these mechanisms in the human observer being the product of learning in addition to innate structure.

The point of these remarks is to suggest that observation is typically structuring sensory input according to what may be called non-conscious beliefs. A given input may well be copied and structured by a number of beliefs, some higher order brain or mental mechanisms then reviewing the question of which structuring seems most revelatory of information about the input. To speak of non-conscious beliefs is to speak of the brain's attaining certain states which could be philosophically articulated as the person's holding certain statable beliefs. (In saying this, it is not necessary to suppose that all of a person's beliefs at any time could actually be expressed in statements.) In other words, what is normally called an observation may be such that many of the beliefs conditioning the statable observation are unconscious. As represented by brain mechanisms, different beliefs might simultaneously be activated by and structure the same sensory input, all at a non-conscious level, with the net result that the input is finally assigned to a belief which seems best to fit it.

Now let us return to our cases. A particular observation may seem anomalous or puzzling because conflicting beliefs can structure the same sensory input and none of these beliefs seems to be a best, or most relevatory, fit. In this situation, resolution may involve conscious wider searching for a belief which will resolve the conflict by structuring the input in a new way, or it could involve non-conscious development of new beliefs until one resolved the conflict, at which point the familiar recognition event (so that's it!) would occur. Beliefs which originally were consciously formulated to resolve some conflict might become embedded as non-conscious brain mechanisms to condition further observation. Again, beliefs originally formulated at a non-conscious level could become consciously articulated for further study after the recognition event if the context seemed to promise repetition of the same kind of conflict in future situations.

Could we not simply have an anomalous sensory input without attempting to reconcile conflicting beliefs about it? Not only could we do so, but we can and do enjoy conflict situations and attempt to retain them, particularly where sensual or aesthetic pleasure is involved. Are there perhaps sensory inputs with respect to which conflicting beliefs cannot be resolved? No doubt there are, but acceptance of this situation, and attempting to avoid it with new theoretical proposals, is probably essential to the distinction between artistic and scientific outlooks. This is perhaps not fair to some artists who may be interested in some situation about which no conflicting beliefs are held, but which is characterized only by rather indefinite or unarticulated beliefs. The scientific outlook, however, is probably always characterized by a desire to fit as many discriminable elements of a sensory input as possible into articulated beliefs. This is no doubt an extension of the natural scrutiny of sensory input until at least the rough significance of the input for biological well-being can be determined.

The other particular case now has an easy treatment. Scientists are not always interested in single anomalous cases. The indefiniteness of the single anomalous event can be expected to show wide variation in more specific content as it is structured by conflicting alternative beliefs. They are *usually* interested rather in observations which already show the regularity of the kind of belief which can be characterized as a theory, law, or hypothesis. This belief may then be subjected to scrutiny to see whether it in turn can be explained by another belief tying it into an integrated system of beliefs. Theoretical proposals attempting integration of this kind are no doubt nearly always conscious in origin. The relative stability of the regularity in the face of alternative theoretical proposals is then to be explained in terms of the fact that the regularity itself is already a consistent, and hence a stable, belief.

Returning now to the notion of objectivity, the solution to its analysis can perhaps now be more carefully discerned in terms of an analysis stressing temporal process. Science is regarded as objective because its overall progress is determined by the structure of an institution in which the rationality of single scientists can widely influence the opinions of other scientists. This is precisely not to hold that the course of science is subject to individual control, but to hold that any man who can propose new theoretical ideas or offer new experimental data can effect a change in the beliefs of other scientists insofar as they behave rationally. The remarks in preceding paragraphs have suggested that scientific beliefs may coincide precisely with human beliefs that can be carefully articulated. A single scientist, articulating a theoretical proposal, thus enables other scientists to try that belief along with their previously accepted beliefs in structuring accumulating data, where such data are taken as analogous to sensory input structured solely by non-conscious or familiar conscious beliefs.

If we agree that scientific practice is objective in terms of its interpersonal structure, can we define objectivity for the individual scientist? Not on any of the usual grounds. It is futile to fall back on a relationship with a fixed external reality, although we do want to discriminate scientific practice from, say, artistic practice. Artistic practice is as dependent as scientific practice on any external reality that may be admitted, and yet we do not normally regard artistic practice as objective. There is no compulsion exerted on artists to test the outlooks of other artists; they are free to develop their own views. Scientific objectivity is to be taken as a feature of total scientific practice in which the practice achieves a nearly continuous adjustment to the accumulating data of scientific observation through the mutual communication and criticism of individual scientists.

The function of criticism here is instructive. A criticized theory in science will typically be *revised.* If the criticism is that of internal contradiction, then criticism is as it is in mathematics, and the criticism must be shown wrong, or the theory abandoned. It might be noted that effective criticism in artistic practice leads typically not to revision, but to the production of new works of art. Mathematical theories can be *developed,* but this is usually taken as the discovery of *additional consequences* about an original postulation of mathematical objects, and not as the addition of new postulates to accommodate unexpected facts. By contrast scientific theories change as they develop, sometimes dropping a statement in favor of another conflicting with it, sometimes adding entirely new concepts, while nonetheless retaining their identity as the same theories throughout the process. In this respect they are analogous to living organisms.

A living organism may adapt well to a fixed environment over a period of time, and this adaptation will usually proceed through steps some of which are non-adaptive false starts, and some of which actively contribute to the adaptive end. Successful adaptation to the environment is a property we can notice only over a sufficiently great period of time, and it is a process which we see most clearly by examination of gross features. (It can be compared to illustrating plant growth and development by showing a movie in which the action is speeded up, illustrating a pattern of development which we would not observe easily under ordinary conditions.)

The objectivity of science seems to be best exhibited by its adaptation to data over a period of time that must be measured from a suitable temporal perspective. To see it as a careful and reasonably continuous adaptation, we cannot look too closely, or we will see confusing setbacks. We cannot look too widely, or we will see only a series of revolutions, with the revolutionary beliefs apparently incapable of being held simultaneously by one individual along with the beliefs of the old order. If we can find a suitable framework for illustrating scientific objectivity over a period of time as an adaptive response to accumulating data, we may look upon the individual scientist as objective if his own career shows similar characteristics on a reduced scale.

We can now return to a discussion of the connection between rationality and objectivity. A single man may be rational in terms of the way in which his beliefs change with changing data. But a rational man may have a rather limited perspective in that he considers only a few alternative hypotheses or theories which seem sufficient for his purposes. The objective man is rational, but he is linked by communication and criticism with the views of other men, increasing the range of alternative beliefs which he may explore. A man's objectivity is derivative from his relationship to other men, but this sense of objectivity does not improperly require that an objective man have a relationship to external reality which can be characterized by some mysterious arbitrator as the man's having a correct description of external reality.

There is one way in which scientific theory might itself be applied to gain an insight into the adaptation which characterizes objectivity as viewed in this chapter. There exists in the scientific literature one theory, the theory of evolution, which deals precisely with situations in which cumulative small discontinuities (not all of them necessarily adaptive or good) can result in rather dramatic variations and gross adaptive transformations over a period of time. This theory gives a coherent account of adaptation (by selection) to an environment over a period of time which is dependent on minute discontinuities. On the grounds that the structure of this adaptation might provide an insight into the development of scientific practice construed as an adaptation by selection to accumulating experimental data, we might attempt to see whether an evolutionary account of scientific practice might provide an account of some features of scientific practice that are poorly explained by any perspective gained from a study of a rationality in a single scientist.

The hope here is obvious. Although the adaptation of a

species is perhaps no more than the sum total of a large number of individual biographies (their successes and their failures), the study of evolutionary theory has largely proceeded by taking the species as a basic category, and studying the adaptation of the species to the environment. In this account, the details of an individual biography may become significant only by contrast to other individuals (actual or possible) who are members of the same species. The individual can hardly be said to be well adapted except by its membership in a well-adapted species, for the individual is simply dead or alive when it is examined, and we cannot take longevity as equivalent to adaptation. Longevity in the individual case can be a consequence of luck. In order to compute the probabilities relevant to a reasonable description of adaptation or fitness, the differential success of suitably similar individuals must be taken into account. We may then suppose by the analogy that the biographies of individual scientists can be regarded as illustrating objectivity only in the context of a consideration of the differential success of all of the other individuals who are attempting to survive and reproduce in the same data environment.

To state the evolutionary point of view as succinctly as possible, we will adopt it in a form which regards scientific theories as analogous to specific species undergoing adaptation in the face of selection pressure represented by the data accumulated in past and current experimentation. A species or theory will typically comprise a variety of genotypes which are in competition with one another against the same environment. In science, these genotypes can be regarded as the variants of a single theory. A theory is to be defined in terms of the range of data to which it responds and to which it adapts. At many points in scientific practice, scientists who accept a single theory in name will prefer slightly different statements of it, or regard it as connected in slightly differing ways to experimental data. These variants may not be divergent enough to be regarded as different theories. Arguments about whether some particular datum follows from a theory can sometimes be traced to conflicting views as to how the generally accepted principles of the theory are to be related to experimental arrangements. Speciation or splitting of theories occurs when new data are provided by new measuring devices or experimental designs, opening up unexplored ecological niches which will first be colonized by slight variations of the old theories before adaptation leads to new theories fitting the new environment very closely, but which would not have competed successfully in the old environment.

It is interesting that the criteria earlier surveyed for the viability of theories fit naturally into this evolutionary account. We might regard falsifiability as a basic condition of viability. Sharply falsifiable theories will be those which fit some environment very closely, but which would not be viable in slightly different environmental circumstances. In biological theory, a species not exceptionally well fitted to its environment may survive provided that it is not everywhere in competition with more well-adapted rivals. It also may survive if it can compete without extinction against a variety of particular rivals who are better adapted to sub-environments. On some philosophical accounts, sharply falsifiable theories are capable of generation for any environment. The criterion of paradigm conservation is also considered as a criterion of viability in order to rule these out. Only those offspring sufficiently like their parents to insure development under parental attention as well as later mating with other individuals are likely to survive, particularly in higher species where parental attention is required for normal development. Paradigm conservation rules out theories which are too ad hoc, either because they will not receive attention, or because they are sterile, that is, incapable of clear modification to handle slightly different data. A mutant gene is a small discontinuity in an older viable genotype which on the analogy does not violate paradigm conservation. A mutation is different because it permits adaptation (or even survival) to a different potential or actual ecological niche than is fulfilled by any current genotype while being embedded in a genotype which gives rise to a viable organism in current environments. Environments discriminate mutants, just as various experiments may discriminate between a given theory and another satisfying the significance criterion by comparison to the first.

We can usefully examine the analogs of both intraspecies and interspecies competition. A good, healthy species will exhibit intraspecies competition in the sense that variant genotypes with roughly the same chromosomal patterns and mechanisms will exist simultaneously within the compass of the same species. Some of these variations may be recessive and largely unexpressed in current environments, but they may be of great potential value to the species in colonizing new ecological niches. The availability of genetic variation for adaptation to new environments expressed in recessive genes is an important dimension of the fitness of any given species. We may expect an analogous kind of variation in scientific theories as well. A given theory as defined in scientific practice should expect to be mirrored in a variety of slightly different axiomatic systems in any full articulation of its range.

Contrary to the opinion of some philosophers, this suggests that it is not *vagueness* in theoretical terms which is then key to adaptation to new environments, but slightly different specific interpretations held simultaneously within the compass of any single theory with reasonable scope. This fact seems to offer a clue to a revised analysis of rationality, for different rational scientists may well adapt to the same data environment with different interpretations of the same theory that are logically in conflict. The existence of these alternatives is then constitutive of a healthy scientific theory and a prerequisite of objectivity. Conflicting alternatives require representation in any adequate logical model for scientific practice. Axiomatic formulations of theories can be seen in this light as analogous to over-adapted species which cannot compete in even a slightly different data environment, but would simply die out. A healthy species or theory is stable in the face of a small change in environment because of the simultaneous presence within its compass of viable variants, although the ratio of these variations accepted by individual scientists may be expected to shift under selection pressure as the environment changes.

As different species may compete for the same living space, we may expect interspecies competition between different theories for various data environments. This competition, biological or scientific, will often exist over a period of considerable time before (if ever) one species completely eliminates the other.

In evolutionary perspective, we can account for the existence side by side of different species, and even different phyla, by looking at appropriate ecological spaces. Very ancient organisms may be found side by side with very recent ones due to the fact that the ancient organism is suitably adapted to a niche which has endured throughout the intervening period of time. We may thus expect, given the analogy, that classical and non-classical theories may exist side by side because they fit different data environments which are still recognizable in the measurements provided by current scientific instrumentation.

The evolutionary view renders coherent the competition between theoretical proposals which is so obvious upon even a casual inspection of the history of science. In terms of overall strategy, the competition increases the rate of efficiency of theoretical adaptation to data environments. Seen in this light, the overall strategy has a direction and objectivity which it may not be possible to discern in an individual biography. Even more interesting, perhaps, is the suggestion that individual error and mistake may not slow down an overall adaptive achievement, and it may even accelerate it by demonstrating the ineffectiveness of some possible adaptive solutions.

So far, little has been said about the exact character of the data environment of a theory. We cannot take observation *simpliciter* as defining the data environment, since the total range of observations made by all scientists will usually be contradictory and will in every interesting case be subject to recognizable sources of error and bias. The environment is partly conditioned by the mechanisms and instruments that are used to make the relevant observations. Just as a change in perceptual apparatus will cause a change in the perceived environment of a living organism, we can expect changes in theory to modify the conception of the data environment to the point where observation may be smoothed out or discarded, provided only that in so doing the theory does not lose control of the environment. In other words, if in the biological situation a change in perceptual apparatus caused a misassessment of the organism's environment, this would be typically shown by the subsequent failure of the organism to compete successfully for the ecological niche. The actual environment is always unknown, and is mediated by perception, but its influence as distinct from the perception of the organism is to be traced in the disappearance of various species. In the scientific analogue, the influence of the environment is to be traced in the disappearance of various theories. The theories may point to an environment which can still be perceived, but the theory is doomed if another theory can compete more successfully in interpreting the observations as conditioned by its concepts and their employment in the proposals of the theory.

In the final analysis, on this view, the analogue to food is control of the environment, and not understanding. No line of demarcation between pure and applied science is consequently to be sought or to be found. Should a theory not make a difference in some data environment leading ultimately to better control of some process with consequential potential benefits for human life, it will not survive the adaptive struggle of scientific development. By means of tracing out this tenuous path, the ultimate relevance of scientific practice to human life can be made out on a philosophically coherent basis.

There is one last point worth gleaning from our biological analogy which points to a way of reconciling the historical and logical approaches to the philosophy of science. In studying the Animal Kingdom, for example, biologists have found it useful to summarize their information about particular animal species by considering an animal as composed of systems such as the respiratory system, the reproductive system, and so on. These systems can be described in terms of the functions which they serve in the living animal. We may approach a strange animal species by asking, for example, how it ingests or absorbs the raw materials for its metabolism, how it eliminates waste products, and how it reproduces itself. These questions can provide a convenient budget of problems for investigation and subsequent exposition. Further, we can feel confident that these questions will be significant in the life cycle of any living animal.

Unfortunately, these questions do not always have an answer in terms of easily identifiable physical structures. The systems may be inextricably entangled in various species, and given structures may perform now one function and then another. In consequence, the answers returned to the questions of the budget for various species may be so different in detail that they cannot be reasonably generalized to provide detailed, interesting, and true descriptions of the reproductive systems of all the animal species which are the subject of scrutiny. This might conceivably be done for the species frozen in a given temporal slice of evolutionary development by devising a suitable classification, but the classificatory scheme would no doubt seem ad hoc, in the light of conceivable evolutionary developments. The substance of biology is to be found in the properties of the individual organisms and species, and not in the framework which may be used to provide a comprehensive exposition of an entire field.

Analogously, logical models seem to raise questions about theories and describe structures at a level of abstraction similar to that assumed in the systems analysis of living organisms. For any theory, it is useful in exposition of its structure to determine what it can explain, or what data seem relevant to its retention. But the detail of the answers, which is the substance of the relevant scientific disciplines, may not fit any more extended general explanatory framework. Logical models may thus be useful as an imposed framework for grasping the structure of each of many divergent theories without yielding information precise and general enough to be regulative for actual scientific practice in view of its possible development as new techniques of investigation are introduced.

The analysis of an organism in terms of systems has the feature that it applies primarily to an analysis of a normal, mature individual of a species. There is no developmental system in an organism in addition to the respiratory system and the other systems used for analyzing its behavior. We may come to understand the development of an organism, but this needs description along lines which are independent of the systems analysis, since the development will typically depend upon a series of different mechanisms and structures over time. Even if specific mechanisms in given organisms are one day explained in terms of a micro-theory utilizing chemical and physical theory, it will be the *differences* between species in the detail of their development and behavior, and not the similarities in chemistry, that will remain as legitimate and unreducible biological subject matter.

The historical models provided by philosophy of science are more clearly biological in spirit. Their intention has been to emphasize interesting peculiarities and differences between theories or between the variants of a single theory, and not to concentrate on the outlines of what may be a relatively trivial organizing framework for classifying an immensely complicated natural environment. It seems that whatever success the logical models may eventually score will not render the detailed examination of the peculiarities of scientific history uninteresting or even obsolete.

Part Two

Science Fiction

Introduction

Part One was concerned primarily with the features of comprehensive philosophical analyses of scientific practice. Scientific practice also affects philosophical practice in other ways. For example, some philosophers have supported various general philosophical arguments by reference to what might one day be incorporated into scientific theory, or to what might one day be invented as a consequence of projected scientific theory. In doing this, some philosophers have not resisted the temptation to talk about the conceivability of a scientist constructing a machine which would unerringly measure and predict all of the brain states of an individual human being. Such a machine would have some rather nasty consequences for various philosophical views, and the nature of philosophical argument is such that even the conceivability of such a machine has nasty consequences for some philosophical views about human freedom. I cannot myself resist the temptation to point out that defending a philosophical position by investing scientists with powers far outstripping their current abilities is no advance on the older but generally discredited philosophical tactic of invoking divine powers to solve otherwise intractable and crucial difficulties with some complicated metaphysical scheme. The investiture belongs properly to science fiction in the one case, theology in the other.

In Part One, it was maintained that scientific practice often embodies an implicit philosophy of science. Philosophical practice, in a similar manner, often embodies an implicit world view to which specific scientific knowledge can be relevant. One might conceivably engage in a line of philosophical analysis of scientific practice without concern about the substantive findings of science. Similarly, one may engage in aesthetic analysis and argumentation at an abstract level without noticing the quality of one's own environment, or engage in ethical analysis and argumentation without assessing the quality of one's own actions. More typically, however, it is to be expected that analysis and its results should lead naturally to substantive views, and to relevant activity.

The substantive views and relevant activity which would seemingly issue from a comprehensive philosophy of science would be some sort of world view or philosophy of nature embracing as much in the way of scientific knowledge as an individual could assimilate. It has been argued that the complexity and magnitude of scientific knowledge makes any such view necessarily incomplete and partial. As Part One should have made clear, this is hardly a conclusive objection, although it is often taken to be one.

Part Two will discuss some of the junctures between philosophical world views and scientific practice that have played a role in the literature of the philosophy of science. The idea in doing this is *not* to take bits and pieces out of various scientific theories, and then string them together into a broad landscape, but rather to find a general outlook which will find a place for traditional questions of philosophy within a reasonably comprehensive world view that is compatible with the general thrust of a wide range of scientific discoveries. It is no good for philosophers to duck this project because of the fact that no one can expect to bring it off without reasonable residual objection. If philosophers won't try, others will simply do it in a worse manner.

Limited in scope as it must be, the discussion which follows is nonetheless designed to counter certain philosophical views which portray a quiet disappearance of general philosophical questions as science develops. For example, if we can indicate the silliness of calls for the reduction through a methodological program of scientific theories to theories of physics, and theories of physics to philosophically determinist theories, perhaps we can establish that humanist concerns and non-scientific knowledge need bear no invidious relationship to current or future scientific practice.

5

Foundations

We can approach the general topic of the philosophical
foundations of scientific theories by a preliminary examination of the graveyard for various logical models of scientific
practice. The biggest mausoleums here undoubtedly belong
to the philosophical views known as *verificationism* and *operationism.* These views are clarified in the following discussion.
It has seemed fantastic to many contemporary students of
philosophy that these philosophies of science could ever have
been taken seriously as explanatory of scientific knowledge,
but this reaction is due to unconscious placement of these
views into something like the current philosophical environment.

Verificationism and operationism attempted to analyze
what they found to be an obvious contrast between scientific
practice and religious or philosophical practice, and they both
found an important source for explaining this contrast in
the supposed precision of measurement in science. Both philosophies must be counted as providing primitive logical
models. They both explained the contrast by viewing scientific practice in temporal slices which could be studied to

see whether they could be regarded as satisfying the features of a logical model proposed as embodying various philosphical desiderata.

An intuitive argument for basic ideas underlying both verificationism and operationism can be provided by the following kind of case. Suppose we disagree (you and I) about whether some nearby object which can be easily manipulated is more or less than two pounds in weight. The disagreement can be easily resolved in this case because we can weigh the object and definitely resolve the dispute. (We won't worry about the case in which the object is almost exactly two pounds.) By contrast, if we disagree as to whether some painting is beautiful, or whether some action is good, it would seem that no rough and ready test by observation or measurement is available. So science may seem at first to be marked out as the area in which disputes can be definitively resolved by observation. If one chooses sufficiently simple examples, this contrast can be heightened until it seems to capture the essence of the distinction between science and non-science.

Operationism further refines the suggested contrast into a reductive pattern. A *term* in the scientific vocabulary is said to have as its meaning just the operations of measurement which constitute a test of the truth or the falsity of the statements in which the term appears. Operationism in this form is quite similar to a venerable epistemological position which seeks to analyze what are ordinarily called *objects* in the physical world into sets of possible sense data which would be equivalent to a given statement about the object in the sense that the statement would ordinarily be regarded as true if and only if the sense data in the set were actually had by perceivers in appropriate perceptual situations.

The philosophical defense of these views is that the truth of any statement about the term or the object cannot in fact be determined save by means of elements in the set of operations or perceptions, so that the truth of the statement seems analyzable into the elements of the set without remainder. In the epistemological tradition, this view is perhaps defensible (even if the sets of perceptions cannot be actually constructed for specific cases) provided that the sense data refer only to visual perceptions, or to sense data from a single sense modality. But we often attribute such things as sights, smells, touches, and tastes to the *same* physical object. In some epistemologies, a faculty of common sense is provided to integrate sense modalities and to realize such common attributions, but there can be no justification for the integration performed by this faculty in the kind of epistemology just mentioned. We can have visual worlds, auditory worlds, and so on, but they cannot be related so as to provide a common physical world of the sort we normally talk about in science without leaving the realm of sense data. Of course, we can give up our ordinary view of the physical world, but it seems more straightforward to take scientific talk as the paradigm and to give up the epistemology as inadequate.

Operationism as a philosophy of science has even greater difficulties than this epistemology. Instead of the sense modalities creating incommensurable worlds of experience, we must take every distinct method of test or measurement as creating a world of operational truths which cannot be suitably combined, by operationist principles alone, to provide a coherent physical world. The problem, in short, is how we are to treat two different tests as tests for the same objective property. Operationists have argued that the relationship of test modalities can be given by an explicit definition, but this definitional process has the flaw that it is not sensitive to scientific development. When we find a new measuring device, we often treat it as a *better* means of measuring an old quantity, and not as changing the *meaning* of the old quantity by enlarging the set of test results which define it. It seems straightforward to keep scientific talk as a paradigm and to give up operationism as an inadequate analysis.

The operationists (at least shrewd operationist scientists like Ernst Mach and P. W. Bridgman) were far from the harmless lunatics that this account may suggest. Careful operationist analyses are often a valuable therapeutic device for examining the scientific status of a term, or for determining the precise way in which statements containing important terms can receive truth determination through experimental results. Such an examination in good hands may clear away mountainous twaddle about the significance of various terms, but an analysis of scientific practice must not merely eliminate twaddle. It has to be concerned with the significance of what is left after the twaddle is gone.

Operationism supposed that the *meaning* of terms could be logically reduced to various *operations,* so that the significance of theoretical terms could be captured in the structure of a temporal slice of scientific practice by suitable definition. Verificationism depended not on an explicit analysis of terms in scientific statements, but on an analysis of scientific *statements* taken as wholes, although it is clear that these philosophies are not unrelated in that scientific statements and the terms in them are not independent. As a result, verificationism and operationism show analogous features. The key idea of verificationism was that if a statement could be established as scientific by its fulfillment of a suitable role in a logical model, then the terms within it could be regarded derivatively as scientific.

Corresponding to operational tests and results, verificationism grounded scientific significance in *observational statements* which were said to be statements attributing some observable scientific property to an observable individual in a manner which could be ascertained by a relatively quick and certain experimental measure. The significant statements of scientific practice were then taken to be the observational statements as well as those theoretical statements which could be related to certain of the observational statements in a manner to be spelled out in the relevant logical model. Unfortunately, verificationism made an assumption that was to prove as fatal as a key assumption of operationism. Operationism assumed that the results of various tests could be determined to an arbitrarily high degree of accuracy. Verificationism assumed that the truth of simple observational statements could be known with certainty as a result of experiment. This may seem no advance at all, but a subtle advantage is gained by the shift. Suppose that an object A is determined to be decisively heavier than an object B on a good balance. Then a simple observational statement about the relative weight of A and B is known to be true, and the truth of this statement is a public matter in that other investigators may verify it by their own weighing procedure. In particular, the truth of the statement can be expected to survive the discovery of a better balance, so that it is not taken as reducible to particular results of particular weighings. On this basis, it seemed to verificationists that the truth of certain observational sentences could form an enduring and cumulative basis for scientific knowledge without having the previously discussed disadvantage of operationism.

Verificationism was not interested in reducing theoretical terms to complex operations. Instead, a theoretical statement had scientific significance if it could be related to observational statements by satisfying the conditions of a suitable logical model. The general outline suggested has the advantage that theoretical terms could thus have significance without being each reducible to specific operational procedures. One simple relationship which seemed sufficient to provide significance for the terms in a statement is the logical pattern of explanation introduced earlier. If O_1 is an observational statement which, in conjunction with a theoretical statement T (but not by itself) permits deduction of another observational statement O_1', then T can be regarded as having scientific significance. Explicitly we can say that the theoretical terms of T receive *partial interpretation* by this means in terms of the observational terms of O_1 and O_1'. To satisfy this requirement in detail, a theoretical statement T, by definition, would have to contain at least one non-observational term, a requirement not necessarily imposed by the model of explanation cited earlier.

Such a term could be called *partially interpreted* because as more connections between observational statements could be found in further explanatory patterns, the term would come to be more clearly defined in observational consequences. If an observational statement O_2 were found to be true as a result of observation or experiment, and to permit deduction of an observational statement O_2' in conjunction with T (but not by itself), then the theoretical term or terms in T would be said to be more fully interpreted because we would understand more of its consequences. All of their considerations were thought by verificationists to be compatible with the suggestion that T could never be shown to be equivalent to any set of observational statements, as long as it retained theoretical status. The possibility of using T to locate more and more connections between observational statements seemed to provide a promising setting for a discussion of development of scientific theories.

Nearly every philosopher who accepted the verificationist position with respect to the partial interpretation of theoretical terms also accepted the view that scientific theories could best be philosophically analyzed as axiomatic theories. Axiomatic theories are discussed fully in logic texts, but here we need only take axiomatic theories as sets of statements defined by taking a few statements (assumed to be true in the intended interpretation of the theory) as *axioms* of the theory, and letting the set of all statements which follow from the axioms by the rules of some logical system constitute the full axiomatic system. Euclidean plane geometry, as is commonly known, is nearly always developed as an axiomatic system by tracing out the consequences of a few geometrical truths taken as axioms. Axiomatic systems may be more or less rigorous, depending on the formal properties of the logical system used to develop them. For our purpose, the important point is that an axiomatic system is a fixed structure of related statements. Such a structure can be found in the analysis of a temporal slice of scientific practice, but it cannot develop or change over a sequence of such slices. At most, one axiomatic system is found to be replaced by another.

The axiomatic construal of theories is closely related to the partial interpretation doctrine, since the latter suggests that statements like T can satisfactorily represent theories. But a theorem of advanced logic was later found to yield the startling result that the partial interpretation view of theoretical terms plus the axiomatic construal of theories entails a difficulty quite like that facing the elimination of theoretical terms by definition in one program of operationism. This result is commonly known as *Craig's Theorem.*

The idea of Craig's Theorem can be given simply as follows. If T and O_1 in conjunction yield O_1', then T by itself will yield the conditional "If O_1, then O_1'." For the *particular* derivation of O_1' from O_1, we could use just this conditional statement rather than T to conjoin with O_1. Of course, we cannot replace T with this conditional in general, since on the partial interpretation view, other explanatory patterns involving other observational statements will also involve T. For example, let O_2' be explained by derivation from the conjunction of O_2 with T. In this case, we could replace T with the conditional statement "If O_2, then O_2'." For just this pair of explanatory patterns, therefore, the *pair* of conditionals "If O_1, then O_1'" and "If O_2, then O_2'" would express the total significance of T.

Now suppose that T can be considered as the sole axiom of a formal axiomatic system expressing a theory. Trivially, one axiom is all that an axiomatic system ever requires, since it can always be taken as the conjunction of the axioms of any other axiomatic system expressing the same theory which has more than one axiom. The theorems (logical consequences) of T can then be generated one by one in a sequence. Our pair of conditionals would appear in the sequence of theorems generated by T. Let the vocabulary used to express T in the appropriate symbolism be divided into two sets of terms, the *theoretical* vocabulary and the *observational* vocabulary.* A statement will be said to be an observational statement if and only if it contains no term from the theoretical vocabulary. Our pair of conditionals would be a pair of observational statements according to the interpretation of T as an axiomatic system.

---

*There would be logical vocabulary as well, but we can ignore that as part of the *form* of the statements which can be expressed in the theory. For convenience of exposition, we are also adopting the view that a theory contains some explicit theoretical terms, and that its generalizations are not derived by logical quantification of matrices containing only observational predicates.

As the theorems of the axiomatic system are generated, we can strike out all but the observational statements, so as to generate a set S_0 of observational statements among which are all of the observational consequences of T. That this could be done was obvious to logicians for a long time, but it seemed harmless since the set S_0 appears ad hoc, and one might expect that it could not in turn always be generated as an axiomatic system by development from a definite set of axioms. However, Craig's Theorem demonstrated that the statements in S_0 could always be given as the theorems of an axiomatic system, a system which could be defined precisely because one could describe the set of axioms for S_0, and one could decide in a finite number of steps whether or not any particular theorem of the original system whose axiom was T was in turn an axiom for the axiomatic system generating S_0.

The axioms for generating S_0 as the theorems of an axiomatic system are infinite in number, but that is acceptable in the study of modern axiomatic systems since there is a decision procedure for determining whether or not an arbitrary formula is an axiom of S_0. In general, one cannot avoid the use of axiomatic systems with an infinite number of axioms in expressing various mathematical systems, and modern axiomatics has developed precise techniques for dealing with such systems. The manner in which S_0 is generated is thus technically no embarrassment to contemporary axiomatics although early verificationist philosophers of science thought of axiomatic systems as always having only a finite number of explicit axioms. But from our perspective, since S_0 is logically tractable as an axiomatic system, Craig's Theorem points out that the original theory axiomatized with the sole axiom T may be replaced by the axiomatic system generating S_0 with no loss of observational content. Therefore, on the partial interpretation view supplemented by the axiomatic construal of theories, there can be *no justification for the intuitive feeling that theoretical terms are an essential and ineliminable part of scientific theorizing.*

To fully grasp this point, we need to remind ourselves of the starting point for verificationism. According to this view, there are many statements of unchallenged scientific status which are called observational statements because they report the objective consequences of various experimental or observational studies. In order to accommodate the patent existence of scientific statements which were not observational statements, verificationists took them to be statements which organized the observational statements into an intelligible pattern as the theorems of an axiomatic system. But non-observational statements were always suspect, and could only have what scientific status could be given them by their role in axiomatic theories. Craig's Theorem eliminates this role. Whatever connection between observational statements is effected by a non-observational statement, we can find an alternate way of making the connection with an observational statement. Non-observational statements are thus at best, superfluous, and if we accept verificationism and the axiomatic construal of theories, we can reconstruct scientific practice solely in terms of the privileged observational statements and logic. To anyone sensitive to the role played by theoretical statements in guiding experimental design and giving significance to the results, this consequence is as awkward as facing operationism. The response must be to modify one of the two views leading to this impasse provided that philosophical considerations seem to oppose a more radical excision of the implicit assumptions engendering the verificationist position.

The standard response of philosophers of science who accept logical models as normative has been to keep the axiomatic construal of theories, and to attempt modification of verificationism by placing more stringent restrictions on the logical relationship to be satisfied in defining the partial interpretation of theoretical terms. The move is motivated by a desire to preserve partial interpretation as a way of discriminating between scientific and non-scientific terms on logical grounds. At this date, no very satisfactory restriction of partial interpretation has been achieved. In view of the remarks in Part One, however, this failure may be regarded as the natural consequence of a completely misguided effort. It would seem more reasonable to give up the axiomatic construal of theories, and to attempt to salvage on a more informal level the legitimate insights involved in partial interpretation.

In addition to the arguments already suggested against the axiomatic construal of theories, the attempt to save it by merely revising the technical definition of partial interpretation is linked to the underlying assumption of partial interpretation that there are incorrigible data statements. This last view is troublesome. If we give it up on general epistemological grounds, a major reason for retaining the axiomatic construal of theories is completely undercut. I propose simply giving up the axiomatic construal as defining fully articulated theories. In doing this, we may still use logical systems to test whether some particular fact follows from a particular *statement* of a theory at some point in its development. This is compatible with the evolutionary viewpoint.

The first step to be taken is to hold that for a typical theory, something like the following is the case. There exists a data environment for the theory determined by observation which exhibits certain regularities and perhaps some singular features which have been and are assessed primarily by observation involving non-conscious beliefs. An explicit account and explanation of these regularities (and singularities, where they seem important) is then provided by various theoretical proposals. A theory is confirmed by these data if by its means the data may be recognized as appropriate, that is, as what one would reasonably expect if the theory were true. If the theory predicts a linear relationship, for example, and the data can be seen as exhibiting a linear relationship, then the data are confirmatory unless some rival theoretical proposal provides a relationship which is different, and which assimilates the data equally well or better. In all cases, the criteria of falsifiability and significance must be satisfied by any considered theory, and the criterion of paradigm conservation is to be satisfied where it is applicable.

The basic fact of the situation is that real observational statements will always involve some possible experimental error. A quantity will be located *within*, let us say, certain limits. But a quantity deduced from a theory is *precise*. (If a theoretical quantity is a precise range of values, rather than a number or other singularity, then the observed range will be expected to fall within certain limits.) Consequently, observational statements simply cannot be *logical* consequences of theoretical statements. Theoretical expectation can thus be compared to ordinary expectation. We expect, let us say, to see someone at a party, but the details of his appearance are often not part of the expectation. Scientific and ordinary observation requires that some features be abstracted and perhaps idealized from the sensory input in order to resolve expectancy into detailed information. This is the root of the failure of the axiomatic construal of scientific theories. Errors of measurement and the limits of observability mean that there is a gap between the consequences of theory and the facts of observation which the relationship of logical consequence cannot bridge. The axiomatic construal may give us an explicit representation of the structure of a theory at a given time, or from a given perspective, but it cannot explain how the data are taken to be relevant to retention of the theory, and this last is simply part of a theory as a theory is considered in scientific practice.

Experimental error and its assessment involve complicated statistical exercises which it is not possible to examine here at any level. Instead, we will look at two ways in which confirmation may occur which are not taken care of in logical models as they now stand. First, suppose that an experiment shows data to be linear and that the only major theoretical proposal to account for the data predicts linear data in an idealized experimental situation which is similar to the actual experiment. Now suppose that a more careful experiment, or an experiment using a slightly more sophisticated measuring device, provides data which are closer to the theoretical relationship than the original data. This kind of confirmation is typically much more important than that provided by repetitions of the original experiment with the same rough experimental error. If data can be accounted for by only one theoretical proposal meeting the criteria of viability, it is likely that the data both *confirm* the proposal (by being similar enough to theoretical proposals to be seen as explained by them) and *falsify* the proposal (by being somewhat different from the actual theoretical proposals). Thus no philosophy of science which depends solely on confirmation or falsification as giving the analysis of the relationship between an isolated theory and fixed data can be completely correct, since actual data are not really precise enough for the one and always satisfy the other due to the same lack of precision.

Once a theoretical proposal has been singled out as the only viable possibility, it is not likely to be regarded as more or less secure on the basis of additional *similar* data. It is hard to find articles in scientific journals whose major claim is to have further increased support for some proposal by running an experiment whose outcome is not significantly different from that of some earlier experiment. (Independent articles reporting similar data may, of course, appear in the journals.) Confirmatory support is increased when a new design or new measuring apparatus brings data into a closer relationship to the claims deduced from some theoretical proposal.

The situation remains similar when two or more theoretical proposals are involved. For simplicity, we consider the case where there are just two rival proposals. An experiment which favors one of these proposals may be followed by a series of further experiments.

Further experiments of a similar nature cannot materially increase the support of the favored proposal. But better experiments based on new measuring devices or better design, and which discriminate even more sharply in favor of the same proposal, will increase its confirmation. There is a problem of dynamics here that logical models cannot satisfactorily discuss. It seems reasonable to say that if the earlier experiments had not been performed, the more accurate experiments would not support the proposal to the same degree as they do when they are seen to refine cruder experiments. In other words, if a number of increasingly precise experiments indicates a trend of idealization toward the data suggested by just one of the viable theoretical proposals, this series is likely to provide more support for the proposal than a single experiment can provide for a single theoretical proposal in another data environment which shows the logical features and precision of the best experiment of the series. (To fully substantiate this claim, it would also be necessary to suppose that the two theoretical proposals show roughly the same level of integration into wider areas of scientific theorizing.) One reason for this is that the worth of an experiment cannot be entirely determined in advance by theory, since we may not have formulated a viable theory at the time when the experiment is planned which would best explain the results that are actually obtained. A number of experiments may first be necessary in order to provide valuable information about experimental design, or to provide information about how the theoretical alternatives should be stated for testing.

There is a cumulative mass of data in the case of experiments conducted over a period of time. In terms of a logical model, therefore, the temporal slice in one area of research shows much greater data resources in terms of cumulative data than a temporal slice in an area where fewer experiments have been run. But this accumulation of data cannot by itself explain the dynamics of confirmation, or why the accepted theoretical view in the one area is regarded as more highly confirmed than that in the other area. As better data become available, scientists gradually discard older data. If the older data are conjoined with the newer data, assuming that the newer data are based on better measuring devices or better experimental design, the older data tend to destroy the precision of the newer data as well as their discriminatory significance. Consequently, *it is not true* (although it is often said) *that experimental data are invariant with respect to temporal translation.* Assuming that an evolution of the universe or relativistic effects relevant to the data are not occurring—another reason why the claim can fail—the data might remain invariant, but their significance for discriminating between proposals seems related to their chronological position in accumulating experimental results.

Unlike the situation reported in many philosophical discussions of confirmation, much of the actual data of scientific practice lies at the outer limits of observability. The structure and character of such data may be so uncertain that no current theoretical proposal can seem very satisfactory. In these cases, a new measuring instrument, rather than increasing the precision of an old measurement, may be regarded as opening up a completely new area to scientific investigation. This kind of discovery in new instrumentation may cause some sort of crisis in the relationship between theory and data.

We will consider first the case where some of the regularities observed in the new data can be correlated with older regularities, but regularities also appear which cannot be so correlated. The natural strategy here is to attempt some sort of extension of the old theoretical proposals to cover the new cases. Where this can be done, the new data environment is seen merely as an increase in extent of the old environment, an increase which is actually confirmatory of the old proposals. For example, some increases in the range of temperature and pressure tended only to confirm the original gas laws of classical physics. Crisis occurs when new regularities are discovered which cannot be accounted for by extensions of older proposals. This situation may be taken to arise when predictions begin to diverge more and more sharply from accumulating data, even when possible experimental error is discounted. Here the new data are taken to provide a new ecological niche, and a new theory may be developed by discontinuous trial and error to fit the new environment. From this standpoint of the new theory, the old regularities may be approximated very closely in certain ranges. Where such approximation occurs, the older theoretical proposals may be left intact as accounting for the most sophisticated data which can be obtained by older methods of observation. Extensions of temperature and pressure revealing van der Waal's forces, for example, did not cause extinction of the original gas laws, but simply a recognition of the limited data environment in which they were viable.

The reason why theories disappear is primarily because they are displaced in some fixed data environment by a better theory. In organic evolution, changes in the physical environment have led to the extinction of species who were unable to adapt to abrupt changes. The physical environment for the development of scientific theory, however, is not known to have changed, although it has been greatly extended, throughout the period of recorded scientific data. We therefore have the situation we observe: classical theories remain after the advent of non-classical theories, and are slowly refined and developed to fit an environment which continues to be given by classical measuring devices. The relevant environments are defined by instruments of perception—first those found in the natural human organism, and then the organism extended by the telescope, the microscope (optical and electron), the centrifuge, the particle accelerators, and so on. A natural history of these means of gathering data would provide the settings for the adaptive processes of particular theories, and for the competition between theories addressing themselves to the same problems. As the advent of reptiles did not mean the extinction of fish, nor of mammals that of reptiles, we can see that the advent of new theories on our biological analogy should not lead us to expect that theories adapted to older environments must disappear. They will disappear only when challenged by a decisively superior proposal in the same environment.

The persistence of classical theory is widely acknowledged, but it is often explained by a notion of convenience. New theories tend to be more complicated in mathematical detail as they are typically proposed to fit more complicated environments. It is therefore suggested that the simpler theory will fit the data well enough to be used for certain purposes even though it can be shown to be inadequate by comparison to its successors. It is then suggested that the successor *could* be used and should correctly be used, but that the time and trouble required would not justify the increased complexity of calculation. Even this seems false, for some calculations well within the reach of some classical theories could not in fact be carried out in the mathematics of their successors because the matter required for storage of information and the time required for the consequent computation would lie outside the limits imposed by our current descriptions of the relevant properties of the universe. In the face of this fact, it seems clear that the argument to the effect that the complicated calculations are possible in principle is of dubious import. The problem now is to find some way of describing how viable theories fitting different data environments can exist simultaneously without holding either that theories are true or false, or that theories bear no relationship to truth, and are merely calculating devices.

We will say that *a theory is true or false by comparison to the features of the data environment to which it is adapted.* A true theory will fit its environment exactly, and theories fitting sub-environments will not fit the same environment as the original theory so exactly, even though correlated regularities establish a relationship between the environments. This situation allows the classical theory to remain viable after the advent of later proposals, without making its semantics depend upon those of the later proposals. It would appear that a sensible construal of the continuing importance of some classical theories is thus incompatible with strong reductionist methodological proposals requiring that truth be measured by foundational theories of some sort.

We can now discuss a familiar question from the literature of the philosophy of science, namely, that of the status and significance of theoretical terms. On the adaptational view of theories, *every* term in a theory is a theoretical term because they are all idealizations used to assess the data environment, and none can fit the data exactly. The purpose of the theory is to provide an internal model—this may be articulated as a mathematical theory which is intersubjective, but still separated from the data environment it models—which provides a coherent structure for the complexity of the data. On this view, there is no reason to hold that the theory must provide a structure underlying the data in some way. A mathematical formalism, for example, which permits one to see a coherent pattern in past data can be regarded by itself as a theory, even if it refers only to observable entities and relationships. Classical dynamics, for example, can be regarded as a theory dealing only with observables in the sense that it describes motions in idealized circumstances which can be suitably tested in the laboratory, but it does not make these motions depend upon, for example, a postulated but unobservable structure of the bodies whose behavior it explains.

On the other hand, some theories do contain theoretical terms in the strong sense that they refer to currently unobservable entities, structures, or relations whose postulated features can provide a coherent account of data in terms of regularities not all of whose features are observable in each datum. At least two illustrations of what this means can be provided by the theory of the gene and the theory of deep structure in modern grammatical analysis. Both theories postulate entities which may not be revealed, and hence observed, in particular data to which the theory is directed. Some of the genetic material of one parent will not be expressed in the offspring, and some of the deep syntactic structure required for grammatical comprehension of sentences in a language will not be expressed in the production of certain sentences. In these theories, a feature is sometimes expressed, sometimes not, but it is always included in the theoretical description so that the theoretical proposal is based on invariant regularities which can always be matched at least in certain respects to the relevant data. A theory which postulates an unobservable mechanism to account for observed regularities is on the borderline between these kinds of theories.

Where an observed regularity involves a relatively large spatio-temporal separation which cannot be bridged by any simple regularity in an existing theory, the temptation is to construct a theoretical mechanism to explain the regularity. This kind of postulation in a situation where the intervening mechanism cannot be observed has been the subject of enormous controversy, because it seems mathematically possible to express the regularity by circumventing any mention of the postulated mechanism, and constructing some regularities involving only observables. The technique for doing this is similar to that described earlier in connection with Craig's

Theorem. Since the mechanism is *postulated,* the basis for its postulation is never sufficient to indicate that the mechanism must be there, or that it must have the postulated structure. This logical fact seems to raise an overwhelming difficulty for any biological analogy between theories and species. If the theoretical entities and postulated mechanisms are eliminable, will they not be eliminated in the struggle for survival? Can a living organism afford the apparent luxury of explaining its environment in terms of factors which determine the nature of the data, but which are not themselves discernible as observed features of the data?

The short answer to this, although full documentation of the answer would be extremely complicated, is that living organisms do afford this apparent luxury. Ethologists have discovered the existence of numerous species-specific behavior mechanisms which are genetically stored for release in the presence of a suitable stimulus. Where these mechanisms are related to survival, an individual organism would not have time to learn how to make an appropriate response in the sense that he would almost certainly be eaten or destroyed first. Mechanisms not so directly related to individual survival, such as reproductive mechanisms, are also too complicated to learn in the span of an individual lifetime, at least with the uniform success of acquisition shown by the individual members of a species.

These observations can be tentatively extended to human behavior. Many philosophers have argued persuasively that at least some conceptual knowledge (roughly, that knowledge can be successfully articulated in language) cannot be acquired by abstraction from the experiences of a single individual. The philosophical and ethological arguments both suggest that an individual has a priori non-conscious mechanisms ready to respond appropriately to suitable stimuli, and mechanisms at least some of which issue in linguistic expression in the human being. These mechanisms are, of course, the result of evolutionary adaptation in the ancestors of the individual. This shift in outlook on the nature of human development, bitterly opposed by older forms of philosophical empiricism, has led to recent experiments providing interesting confirmatory evidence for the truth of its general outlines.

In recent experiments, T.G.R. Bower has demonstrated that human infants forty to seventy days old show considerable perceptual skill that they could not have abstracted on classical empiricist theory from their early experiences. For example, such an infant sees a fixed object as having the same (physical) size regardless of its distance, even though the retinal size varies considerably with varying distance. Again, the slant of a flat-sided object not perpendicular to the line of sight could be discriminated by these infants from an object perpendicular to the line of sight having the same retinal shape. It does not require much reflection on the possible evolutionary line of development to see that the perception of constant size and the orientation of flat objects to the line of sight would have rather high survival value.

If we accept the general conclusion of ethological findings suggesting that each individual of any higher species of animal life will have a number of species-specific innate behavior mechanisms, we can also see that these mechanisms exhibit some of the characteristics of theoretical proposals and of perceptual mechanisms that have already been mentioned. In particular, these mechanisms must somehow be neurally modeled in a form containing elements not actually discriminable in sensory input, but which are required to give significance to sensory input. The function of significance here is, among other things, to provide a systematic expectation of the near future. An individual's experience is probably too thin in content to provide the basis for reliable expectation of the future in many cases. Suppose that we each developed our own conceptual framework on the basis of our own experience and abstraction from that experience in conformance to the requirements of the logical models of scientific practice. Although this judgment requires the delicate balancing of many factors, it seems fair on reflection to say that human behavior would be much more varied, and would show much more variety in response to similar stimuli, than in fact it does. The similarity and reliability of our own behavior in the face of various stimuli is to be accounted for largely by means of the massive influence of the experience of our evolutionary ancestors as represented in various genetic mechanisms which can be successfully applied to a relatively stable biological environment.

In view of this line of thinking, theoretical terms can be regarded as giving significance to sensory input in order to provide a systematic expectation of the future, at least the near future. Both kinds of theoretical terms—those which can be discriminated as corresponding to elements of sensory input, and those which cannot, but are required to give significance to sensory input—have exactly the same status. If theory is excised, one is left with just data, and no means of systematically extending the present data into a coherent expectation of the features of new data.

Once the temporal aspect of a theory as a means of adapting to a data environment has been eliminated in representation of the theory as an axiomatic system, it is not surprising that theoretical terms should seem to have no significance. It is interesting in this respect that axiomatics has such a domineering status in mathematics. The environment does not change in mathematics through the use of new measuring devices; it is created as an immutable abstract object through postulation. Therefore, adaptation to an environment over time is not an important feature of mathematics: the integers are what they were for Plato, but the physical universe has changed. Mathematical axiomatics and physical theory come very close together when a physical theory becomes classical. The means of measurement in a classical theory are generally so well explored that the data environment is not expected to show a change. Under these circumstances, it approximates an object of mathematical investigation, since the features of successful theory can then be postulated as mathematical entities, and the theory cast into axiomatic form.

In comparing theories and species, we have based analogies on a prior understanding of biological species and biological evolution, and we have indicated that species are to be studied by the comparative study of idealized mature organisms. What are the individuals which comprise a theory? They are not the individual scientists who examine or accept it, but the different interpretations of a theory which can be regarded as adaptive mechanisms, and studied by a comparative method. From the standpoint of linguistic evidence, however, a theory seems treated as though it were a single entity of some kind: *the* special theory of relativity, *the* theory of the gene, and so on. This fact contributes to the seductiveness of the axiomatic construal, but it too can be profitably compared to our talk about species. We speak of such things as The Great Northern Pike and The Dandelion. Of course, at times, the subtlety of phenotypic differences may escape ordinary or folk classification, but we need only consider at the moment those species identified by biological taxonomy which have equivalent definite descriptive names in English.

Philosophical theories of descriptions are typically inadequate to deal with these cases in their usual treatment. "The Great Northern Pike has two eyes" does not say that every Great Northern Pike has two eyes, but that the idealized Pike used for purposes of recognition of the species in particular specimens does have two eyes. In this sense, the ascription of a property to a species *is* ascription to an individual, but not to any actual individual nor to all individuals which can be recognized as members of the species. The logic of this has not been carefully worked out because the situation has had limited application in the context of logical models. Failure to have a satisfactory philosophical theory of these descriptions should not blind us to the way in which reference to species is perfectly intelligible in a proper biological context.

Our analogy between species and theories seems well supported by the way in which information about either one is communicated. To learn about either, we examine specimens, organisms in the one case, or interpretations (possibly axiomatic) in the other. We can conjointly study the idealized structure and mechanisms used to identify the specimens which have been proposed by past scientists. In species, this means a discussion of organic systems and behavioral mechanisms distinctive of the species. In theories, this means a discusion of the special concepts of the theory and the mechanisms by which these concepts are related. This can be suitably illustrated by example:

"The quantum theory may be characterized by the following features:
(Q. 1) A system is represented by a vector in Hilbert space. . . ." (See [B12], p. 193.)

"Morgan summarized his views in *The Theory of the Gene* . . . the following is a paraphrased rendering of his formulation: (i) the characters of the individual are referable to paired elements (genes) in the germinal material, held together in a definite number of linkage groups. . . ." (See [R1], p. 232.)

These statements are quite similar to idealized descriptions of species in terms of general principles such as circulatory, metabolic, and reproductive systems. A number of slightly different variants of each theory which can be regarded as different interpretation, is obviously possible. From the quotations, we cannot *determine* the specific vector for a fixed system, nor the specific pairing and linkage groups for a fixed organism. Differing interpretations will propose different vectors and different linkage groups for specific cases, while being regarded as statements encompassing the key ideas of the given theory. But both of these theories demand a certain kind of discrete representation in their statements which was not found in other competing theories at one point in scientific development, so that the descriptions do provide identifying constraints upon any interpretation of the theory.

In addition to theories as such, that is, proposals referred to as *the* theory of thus and so, there are many references in the scientific literature to areas of scientific practice which are not described as particular theories. Molecular genetics, statistical mechanics, relativity theory, and quantum theory will serve as examples. These are not theories as such, but rather wider areas of scientific investigation which we will take as analogous to the classes, order, and so on of biological taxonomy. Each such area will contain numerous theories without itself being a theory.

A taxonomy of natural kinds is patently suitable in biology. Is it suitable as well for the taxonomy of scientific theories?

To see the significance of this question, we may compare it to an area in which a taxonomy of natural kinds is clearly impossible. A suitable area is that of the manufactured goods of an industrial society. These goods may be nearly arbitrarily changed or distorted. We can cross one with another by a simple separation and recombination. The engine of an automobile will function in the body of another under very minor constraints and with a minimum of alteration. Arbitrary crossing of living organisms with the same freedom is much more difficult. The reason for this lies in the adaptation of organisms and of theories to fixed environments, so that viability in an environment can be easily destroyed by arbitrary tampering. In manufacturing, there is no fixed environment determining viability, at least not in the short run. One can make various items just for the fun of it. Similarly, one could construct what appeared to be a theory, or a specimen, out of bits and pieces of others, but neither would be viable if certain natural constraints were violated. We have already looked at some of these constraints in our conditions for viability.

In this chapter, we have attempted to apply some of the insights of the evolutionary viewpoint to some of the traditional problems of the philosophy of science. The point in doing this is to demonstrate that the evolutionary viewpoint provides analyses which are suitably general, yet which seem to conform with the details of scientific practice at many interesting points. This demonstration, while it does not exhaust the detail of the kind of analysis which the evolutionary viewpoint can provide, does seem sufficient to prove that the viewpoint is not *vacuous*. The evolutionary viewpoint leads to positions which are discriminable from those which have been provided by historical and logical models, and which are in many respects superior. In the last two chapters, we will discuss some issues on which both scientific knowledge and philosophical analysis seem to bear. These issues are important, and it is a welcome result that the evolutionary viewpoint seems to lead to viewpoints on these issues which are intuitively preferable to some of the austere consequences of other philosophies of science.

6

Space and Time

Space and time provide the framework within which we order perceptions, and by means of which we comprehend the unfolding of various physical processes. As abstractions, space and time are represented by variables or parameters in the mathematical statement of various physical theories. The role which these variables and parameters can play in the mathematical statement of a theory can vary considerably with the data environment that the theory adapts to. In classical theories, space and time were often treated as abstractions serving to provide a neutral and universal framework for describing certain observations. To assign a place to a body or a temporal instant to an event was an activity as arbitrary as putting numbers on a group of shirts to be laundered and returned to their owners. In both cases, certain ordering constraints would have to be satisfied, but these could be satisfied with a wide variety of actual indices. In more recent theories, such as various versions of relativity theory, space becomes a field with entirely different properties. These properties are not independent of various temporal considerations, and they may either influence various properties of bodies, or they may even be actually constitutive of them. Philosophers and physicists have also suggested that the spatio-temporal notions known from classical physics are completely unsuited for theoretical purposes in quantum physics dealing with strong interactions. In the face of these varying views, it seems quite certain that no general philosophical accounts of space and time are likely to prove adequate for the total range of scientific speculation. Space and time, like the conception of an environment, may turn out to be related closely to the details of development of a particular theory.

What threads of similarity could link spatial, temporal, or spatio-temporal variables in diverse theories? The whole topic is closely related to the expectation of the future provided by a theory. Not all theories are explicitly mathematical in the appropriate sense, but let us consider a classical, mathematically explicit theory. In such a theory, it is not thought necessary to determine by experiment which variables are spatial and which are temporal. Instead, it is first observed how some well-defined physical situation changes either by its own natural development, or as the consequence of a controlled manipulation of the system. A mathematical formulation then contains variables such that, if a physical system of the appropriate kind has certain observed properties at a given place and a given time, then the observed properties at another place and time can be calculated by substitution of the appropriate values for spatial and temporal variables which describe the first place and time. The special status of spatial and temporal variables is usually marked by the use of special typography (x_1, x_2, x, t, etc.) to indicate how these are germane to a prediction of a new state of the system. Values for these variables are provided by rulers, clocks, or whatever, whose workings are thought of as independent of the system being studied.

Far from being abstracted from the data, temporal development and possible spatial location are classically conceived of as independent of the data, that is, as providing a neutral framework for the description of the data. The concepts of temporal change and spatial location are apparently given a priori (innately) to human beings as a result of the evolutionary process and these concepts are used to interpret or give significance to what is perceived. This would be the *basis* for the use of spatial and temporal variables, even though their sophisticated use and the measurement of particular values would be augmented in scientific practice by mathematical techniques and by developments in measuring instrumentation. The discovery of biological clocks and orienting mechanisms as an illustration of the way in which spatial and temporal variables may be controlled by an organism is also supported by various epistemological arguments. A successful predicting mechanism, say a device for automatically directing anti-aircraft fire, must contain a suitable internal representation of temporal and spatial sequences if it is to bring an explosive into close contact with a target. If it depended just on the sequence of positions of an aircraft, the explosive might arrive too early or too late to make successful contact. The predicted location of the aircraft to which the explosive is directed depends upon taking the sequence of observed positions as instances in a suitable temporal sequence. We may similarly expect from food-gathering activities alone that some innate spatio-temporal mechanisms would appear in a wide variety of living organisms. The problem is to see how these mechanisms, articulated and refined as conscious human concepts during the development of modern science, play a role in modern physical theory.

One difficulty is provided by an extension of the previous observation that the idealized concepts of theory must be recognizable in the inexact measurements which test or support a theory. Is the discovered discrepancy to be regarded as though the theory and the environment were in some sense each exact, but linked by a measuring technique or observational technique which, partly as a consequence of human incapacity, would inevitably obscure a theoretically precise relationship between theory and environment? This problem is very close to the nest of problems known as philosophical determinism.

Let a theory be such that if certain exact values are supplied for a mathematical representation of the theory, one can predict by calculation another set of exact values for a later time. Such theories are called *deterministic*. Most physical theories have been deterministic in this sense. If observed or measured values are supplied from observation of some system, a check of a prediction made by a deterministic theory will typically show greater and greater discrepancy with later observation and measurement as the temporal gap between the determinations of the values lengthens.

There are two important factors which help to explain this universal difference between theoretical values and observed values. To illustrate the first, imagine simply that we are calculating the spatial separation of two bodies which are moving along straight-line paths as a function of time. Relevant details aside, we can assume circumstances such that if the initial paths are parallel, the spatial separation will be invariant. But imagine the paths slightly divergent. We can assume circumstances such that even the slightest divergence will cause a spatial separation of any possible magnitude after sufficient time has elapsed. Suppose our observation is that the paths are parallel, but due to experimental error, they are nonetheless slightly divergent. Our prediction of their separation in the future will become less and less accurate as time elapses. Thus even a very small error of measurement combined with a precise deterministic theory, even on the assumption that the theory fits the environment exactly, can produce a totally unreliable prediction of events in the distant future. Error of measurement, therefore, is a presumably ineliminable source of failure of deterministic prediction with elapsed time.

In addition to error of measurement, a deterministic theoretical prediction, to be precise, must be based on a *sufficient* set of initial values. The usual way to put this is to say that such predictions are precise only for closed or isolated systems. For example, considering the moving bodies of the last example, an initial divergence will result in extensive spatial separation later, provided that no force or other factor intervenes during the interval to cause the paths to become parallel or to converge. A closed system is by definition a system subject to the influence of no forces, bodies, or whatever outside the system (on the exterior of the spatial extent of the system) during the interval that it is regarded as closed. In theory, a completely closed system must be isolated thermally, gravitationally, electrodynamically, and so on from every other system. In practice, clearly, there are no completely closed systems, and the residual influence across the boundary of any system being studied, no matter how relatively well isolated it is, can be expected to interfere with the precision of a prediction based on the exclusion of such influence. In practice, systems are studied which are closed to those influences which seem relevant to a change in value of the variables of the system which are being studied.

The abstraction to a theory using precision classical notions of space and time can thus result in a literally insoluble philosophical problem. Theory and environment could match exactly, but due to error of measurement in applying theory, theory and environment could come to disagree in the values of certain variables which interest us as severely as we can imagine. Since this error is ineliminable, the fit of theory to environment is not capable of an exact determination. In practice, this fact is probably involved in the willingness of scientists to adopt theories whose predictions remain accurate to within some desired degree with occasional corrections due to new measurements.

So far, we have treated measurement and observation as somewhat equivalent activities. In a sense, this is all right, since measurement and observation both involve a similar interaction between two systems. Although a machine or instrument is said to measure or observe something, this usage is undoubtedly an extension of human observation or measurement. The human observing or measuring system is not closed, since the human *is* subject to constant influence from his environment, but this influence is often shielded from various internal systems of the human being in a manner which renders that influence (practically) irrelevant.

Strictly, to test a deterministic prediction, a human being

must observe or measure the relevant values of some closed system which is part of his environment. Turning viewpoints around, the human observer must be regarded as part of the environment of the closed system. An observation across the boundary of the closed system is a logical impossibility. Some transfer of information from the observed or measured object or process to the human must take place, so that the boundary *is* traversed in some way, in violation of the definition of a closed system. We tend to call an observation any acquisition of information by human beings in which some transmission originating in the system is interpreted by the observer without his responding by a transmission to the observed system which changes the state of the observed system. A star or a large physical object can be observed if the observer merely interprets light signals, auditory signals, or whatever from the observed system. To be sure, the object observed has now lost some photons, or has had some photons bounced off it, or whatever, so that in terms of a philosophical notion of identity, we could generate a little paradox to the effect that we can never *observe* something exactly as it is.

This paradox is pretty flaccid if one accepts the contention permeating this book that an object does not differ from its state as observed in any way that matters to scientific practice, unless the perceptual apparatus of the observing organism is defective. A large physical object that has lost some photons can be described as different, but we can also know in terms of the relevant theory that this difference is irrelevant to certain predictions of the theory (or at least that it makes no difference in prediction which could be observed), and hence that it is an irrelevant difference. From the standpoint of physical theory, the object *is* the observed object, and minor variations given by one theory in an object over a period of time or between two objects at the same time would be recognized as identity of objects within the framework of the theory used for prediction in the relevant instance. The *basic insight* is that observation of an object can be carried out in many cases in ways which do not change it in any theoretically significant way.

By contrast, measurement implies doing something to the measured object, and observing the result. Measurement is a two-way interaction between the measurer and the measured. Here the measured object as observed is known not to be the same as it was before measurement. The seriousness of this depends upon the magnitude of failure of closure imposed upon the measured system by the measuring signal. As is well known, this failure of closure may not be irrelevant in terms of the theory one might wish to use in prediction. The Heisenberg uncertainty relationships are a now classic illustration. In addition to error of measurement, therefore, the failure of closure introduced by measurement as accurate as we could theoretically carry out insures that deterministic predictions about closed systems whose relevant values must be measured will not always coincide with the data environment, even if the usual sources of error in the measured value are assumed to be absent.

With the exact nature of determinism still left unclear, we can see nevertheless that there is no way of demonstrating an exact fit between a theory and a data environment where the fit must be estimated by measurement. In view of this situation, what makes a theory deterministic in any useful sense? A theory usually involves description of some entities which the theory is about, and it provides this description by ascribing some number of properties to each such entity. When a description of an entity referred to by a theory contains a value for each of the properties which may be ascribed to it in the theory, we will say a *state* of the entity has been defined. For simplicity, we consider only those theories involving a mathematical formalism in which the variables describing the state of a closed system can be given as a mathematical function, and the development of the state of the system over time can be given as an additional mathematical function of the original function defining the state and a temporal variable. If, for any length of time such that the system remains closed, one can calculate the state of the system at any other instant of this length of time, then the theory is said to be deterministic. Failure of this condition in a theory makes it indeterministic. Both determinism and indeterminism, therefore, are properties of theories, and not properties of the data environment. It should be noted in particular that a theory may be deterministic even though we could not determine the state of a closed system described by the theory as a result of measurement closely enough to determine its state as measured at some other time to within a preassigned degree of accuracy, no matter how small.

A causal theory can be regarded as a special kind of deterministic theory. As remarked at the end of the last paragraph, the theoretical state of a system may not be measurable to arbitrary accuracy, perhaps because measurement of one state variable makes determination of the simultaneous value of another state variable impossible within the limits of assigned accuracy. Suppose, however, that we can bring a single system repeatedly into the same state within some preassigned level of accuracy, or we can create a number of systems all of which are in the same state. We regard the state so obtained as a starting point. In the former case, if the system develops the same way each time as assessed by later measurement of the state to the same level of accuracy that characterizes the starting point or to a precise initial precision of measurement, we will call the system *causal*. In the latter case, we may need to consider spatially isolated systems existing at the same time whose precise spatial coordinates do not matter. If each of these develops according to the criterion mentioned above, the theory describing their development will also be called *causal*. According to these definitions, the time at which a system is in its starting point does not matter, so that temporal translation does not affect the development of the system. In the other kinds of theories, whose development may be evolutionary, the time at which a system is in its starting point does matter. In some causal theories, theoretical entities used to explain a causal sequence could travel in a reverse time sense to the sequence, provided that the properties of such entities are not part of the states which define an observable starting point or an observable later state.

The concept of a starting point in a causal theory indicates that causal theories depend upon a preferred temporal direction. The starting point is always first cause. Plants of a given strain may be brought repeatedly into a state in a closed system such that, for example, a precise water and mineral intake is part of the definition of the state. We may calculate a certain growth from such a starting point under the correct conditions. There are two reasons why the reverse calculation may not make sense. First, we may or may not be able to deduce the starting point from an observed growth. Although the original starting point may lead to a narrowly defined range of growth, the same stage of growth may be obtained from other starting points by different conditions of watering, providing minerals, and so on. We could not determine a starting point from the growth, so that the system could not be considered if one wished to reverse it. Secondly, in this case, reversal is not possible. No one has done it, and no one can conceive how it might be done. Even if only one small range of states was compatible with the observed growth, and we could calculate this from the growth, we still could not put the plant into the growth state as a starting point, and later observe it less developed, discharging, among other things, water and minerals from its roots.

Causal theories have often been central to philosophical discussions of scientific method because they seem to reveal properties (temporal direction) of the environment in a manner in which non-causal deterministic theories cannot. On the other hand many philosophers of science have felt that causality arises only because of the way in which the human biological clock operates or because of features of human consciousness. It is an interesting question whether scientific theories can be stated entirely in non-causal ways which make no reference to a privileged temporal direction. On the view holding that this is possible, it has seemed that our biological clocks give us a direction in time which is that in which we *happen* to be evolving, but it has also seemed conceptually possible that we might meet sentient creatures with a reversed time sense. This situation boggles the imagination, but we can obtain it as a consequence of holding that classical deterministic theories are sufficient to describe the scientifically relevant features of the universe. The subject is worthy of closer scrutiny.

Suppose we allow a ball to roll down an inclined plane from a fixed starting point as frequently as we wish. The positions of the ball after release on the plane may be plotted against elapsed time, and a well-known mathematical function can be stated whose predicted values will lie quite close to the observed values in careful measurement. Now, although the ball always rolls *down* the plane in this experiment, we can reverse the state of affairs in the mathematical theory, using the same equation with temporal coefficients of opposite sign or by substituting different values into the same equation to solve for positions of the ball if it were taken to be decelerating but rolling *up* the plane due to the application of some unknown force. This conceptual reversal is far from easy to bring about in actual practice, but we could rig up an apparatus such that the ball would roll up the plane in accord with the mathematical theory.

In a more complex situation, we can have a container divided by a partition into two compartments, one without a specific gas and the other containing that gas. After removal of this partition to obtain a starting point and the lapse of sufficient time, the container will reach an equilibrium state in which the gas molecules are distributed uniformly within the space of the container according to a mathematical theory which can be appropriately applied to this case. Again, the mathematical equations could be used to solve the reverse problem by predicting the location of the molecules in one side of the container from an initial position of uniform distribution. The experimenter could rig up an apparatus to demonstrate the reverse process if he could manage to reverse the paths of the molecules. Let there be only two such molecules. Then the situation is fairly trivial, and the experimenter may have some chance of actually effecting the reversal. (This is all science fiction, since the molecules would have to be found, their paths calculated and reversed. In practice, one would have to be very lucky to bring this off.) But the more molecules involved, the more difficult the reversal is to obtain, even though the reversal of the mathematical description is as precise as it was in the simple case. The irreversibility of processes involving a large number of molecules in this fashion, an irreversibility which can be correlated with a causal theory on a level where such factors as temperature and volume are measured directly instead of the motions of molecules, is thus attributed to human inability to effect reversibility experimentally.

Irreversibility and causality may then be said to be "fact-like" rather than "law-like," meaning that the irreversibility is not expressed in the mathematical features of the laws involved, but in contingent matters relating to boundary conditions, measurement, and available equipment. On this view, human beings may not be able to reverse certain processes, but they are reversible in the sense that the mathematical theories can be solved with a different temporal sequence, and instances of these other solutions elsewhere in the universe cannot be ruled out by any known laws. The upshot of this is that the irreversible passage of time which we experience must be simply a mistaken transfer of a feature of our psychological makeup to a feature of the universe.

In support of this view, it can be pointed out that most of the mathematical theories used in the scientific description and forecasting of physical processes are reversible. If we adopt a reductionist view that all processes are to be explained in terms of physical laws, then we must suppose that causality, wherever it might appear, is a misleading and anthropomorphic way of describing an essentially reversible and non-causal process. But this difficulty may be manufactured equally by an illicit shift from talk about theories to talk about the environment which the theories are used to model. As has been suggested, both deterministic and indeterministic theories may be fitted to suitable environments within the limits of experimental confirmation, so that we cannot conclude from the reversibility of a suitable physical theory that processes in the physical environment are themselves reversible. All we require of the theory is that it give suitable results when it is *intelligently* used.

In a mathematical representation, there is nothing distinctive about temporal variables except our interpretation of them as such. If a function can be described as linking some set of states with a sequence of temporal states in a many-to-one or one-to-one fashion, the same states could be linked with the reverse sequence of temporal states to create another function. Once we have chosen a mathematical representation, this kind of reversibility is trivial provided only that the original function fits the normal definition of a mathematical function. Most of the functions which can be graphed in the ordinary sense with a temporal variable as ordinate or abscissa can be reversed by rotation about the appropriate axis. The mathematical tractability of these functions has resulted in their use wherever possible, and history confirms that this has been possible in an extremely wide range of cases.

Once we have found a mathematical representation or model for a theory, we usually have a symbolic structure that we can play with at leisure. It is quite like having a set of slides illustrating the development of an animal, or a movie film of some ordinary activity. We can reverse the slides or the film, and it can seem difficult to find a convincing theoretical reason why the reversed model couldn't correspond to an actual occurrence somewhere in the universe, or in some universe.

A man throws a ball to another man who catches it. We make a film of this and run it backward. However, this situation is really quite unlike the often discussed case of a particle being omitted from one source and absorbed by another, the passage of the particle being treated as a signal of some kind. We can represent this case of the particle as two points in a suitable space, and a directed line connecting them. It is easy to reverse the direction of the line in this abstract representation and consider the logical possibility that the particle passes in the other direction. The direction of the line is simply reversed in the representation. What about reversing the flight of the ball? Actually, if we do so even in fantasy, the ball must accelerate without application of any known force. Therefore, the reverse flight prima facie violates the known classical laws of physics applicable to the situation, and we would have to discover new forces to account for it. Again, the muscular structure and other anatomical features of the humans involved are maladapted in the reversal in a manner which conflicts with biological law. In both of these cases, the relevant laws cannot receive an entirely mathematical representation, since their application depends upon abstraction from situations in which the biological sense of time confers an antecedent privileged direction. This remains true when the data used to gain an instantiation of the laws to solve a problem are represented as a mathematical statement.

Reversibility and irreversibility thus depend entirely on the theory in question and upon the level of analysis which is contemplated. But this situation seems awkward for reductionists, since it would appear that the time involved in all scientific theories ought to be the same if scientists are to be talking about the same physical universe, and this time should either have an intrinsic direction or it should not. On this strategy, if there is a basic reducing physical theory, its conception of time must be regarded as fundamental and must be regarded as settling the issue of the directedness of physical time. This conclusion would in fact hold if there were a universal physical time, as was postulated in classical theories. But in relativity theory, for example, while there is a conception of time measured by the clocks of observers, there is no universal time in the classical sense. As is well known, the temporal order of two events in relativity theory may not be absolute, but may depend upon the reference frame of the observer who records the order. Because of this, many particular observations of temporal order lose their significance in relativity theory, and only scientific laws not depending upon such orders can be regarded as invariant between different observers. Even more mysteriously at first acquaintance with the idea, an event which takes a finite length of time on the clock of one observer may in certain circumstances take an

infinite length of time on the clock of another observer.*
Consequently, time scales for various observers may be simply
incommensurable, even though this incommensurability can
be perfectly accounted for by rigorous derivation from the
theory.

This illustrates an important fact that cannot be overly
stressed. Our ordinary conception of time used for purposes
of biological survival may be suitably extrapolated (and was
so extrapolated) to the data environment of classical theories
of physics. In these cases of extrapolation, time is irreversible
because its direction is always determined in practice by an
irreversible biological clock. Classical reversible mathematical
theories describe processes which could conceivably occur
in either direction or they may provide descriptions of an
irreversible process which is perfectly useful because we can
determine the proper direction for the temporal variable. We
cannot tell which. But for purposes of investigation of the
very large and the very small, our notions of time based on
extrapolation from biological clocks simply break down. In
cosmology and particle physics, our intuitive notions can
lead directly to contradiction when they are taken in conjunction with other well-established laws. The significance of
one event following another simply disappears, since they may
vary from different observers, or may be indeterminable because of uncertainty relationships.

We can profitably return here to the distinction between
open and closed systems. It may be that the study of either
an isolated fundamental particle or of the entire universe is
in effect a study of the same closed system. The mathematical equivalent might be the consideration of an area, which
in suitable cases remains the same whether or not a point,
or any finite set of points, is or is not included among the
points of the area. In the case of a fundamental particle, the
absence of postulated internal structure means that the environment contains all of the information in a situation involving
it. In the case of the universe, the absence of postulated en-

---

*There is an informal introduction to this situation in *The Riddle of Gravitation*
(Scribner's, New York, 1968), Peter G. Bergmann, Chapters 13–15.

vironmental structure means that all of the information in the situation is contained in terms of a description of the internal structure of the universe. Both situations are degenerate or limiting situations in which temporality may play no significant role. For example, an assessment of change depends upon comparing some invariant standard against features of the changing object, and this requires some sort of distinction to be drawn between the observer and his standard as opposed to the changing object. In the case of the individual particle, its identity and its properties along any conceivable temporal direction are completely overwhelmed by the environment. In the case of the universe, its identity and its properties along any conceivable temporal direction are incapable of measurement against any external standard. Although these remarks would have to be expanded and qualified in a fuller treatment, classical distinctions between space and time are clearly not tenable for certain purposes in the physics of the very large and the physics of the very small.

Now we can consider physical systems with describable internal structure which also have a complex environment. If such a system is closed, we expect it to show various invariants over a lapse of time. When such a system is opened, however, these invariants are no longer stable, and, in general, the physical input or output affects the properties of the entire system. In Newtonian systems, for example, the change in spatial position of a single particle of a previously closed system due to transmission of a force across the boundary of the system results in an instantaneous change in position of all of the other particles of the system. In systems described by field theories, the change is not instantaneous, but in a calculated time the effects of opening the system will be felt everywhere.

Now let us consider living systems, in particular human beings. Much has been made of the fact that living systems are open systems, requiring energy from their environment in order to carry out metabolic processes. Unlike most strictly physical systems, a living system may develop in such a manner that it shows increasing organization (and hence decreasing entropy) over a period of time in which it consumes (and destroys the organization of) various foods. A decrease in entropy in living systems is not known to violate any thermodynamic principles in view of this open relationship with the environment. It should also be emphasized that living systems are *closed,* or more properly, contain closed or nearly closed sub-systems within their boundaries. We have already pointed out that closed systems can only approximate isolation from their environment. Within this perspective, hereditary material constitutes a closed system within an organism which cannot be controlled by the individual and which is highly resistant to outside physical influence.

Indeed, the closure of systems of hereditary material is of a very interesting kind. If the system is opened, the viability of the material is very sensitive to influence, so that only very minute changes are compatible with viability, otherwise viability is destroyed. Effective closure of a system designed to obtain some end is obtained when the structure of the system collapses completely under a sufficiently wide opening, so that instead of a wrong end being obtained, no end is sought or obtained because the system loses distinction from its environment. Devices for closure in this fashion must be very important in reaching any ultimate explanation of a distinction between living and non-living systems. A less obvious example of closure is to be seen in the case of concepts. They remain relatively invariant in structure over time in the face of impingement on the total living system of various stimuli through the channels of perceptual mechanisms.

An individual living organism marks out a reasonable separation between itself and its environment for the purpose of survival. Its internal structure must be complex enough to include relatively closed sub-systems at least some of which are used to provide recognition of similarities or invariances in the external environment. The difference between living and non-living systems will as a result lie at least partly in principles of organization which permit the decoupling and effective closure of selected sub-systems from the energy exchanges involved in metabolic openness to the environment. As such organization is not found in physical systems, we can expect the analysis of living systems to display principles of organization which may be compatible with physical law, but which are not currently known. The discovery by von Neumann of principles of organization which can permit self-replication in *sufficiently complex* machines situated in an appropriate environment constitutes a case in point. These principles were not a simple consequence of any known computer program or physical principles of organization.

Organizational principles distinguishing clear cases of living from non-living systems have not been offered here because they have not yet been satisfactorily formulated. In a sufficiently simple physical system, a given change in some variable will typically affect the value of at least one variable of every element of the system. In more complicated physical systems, we can have a change in some variable not affect the value of variables of related parts. A computer memory bank may have a change in the number stored at some address without affecting certain programs or without affecting other numbers stored at other addresses. Living organization is even more complex. Failure of certain parts can be entirely circumvented. A given stimulus can seemingly be considered by a living system, and then vanish without leaving any trace in memory or behavior. Each specific feature of this kind *can* be matched by a physical system. There may consequently be no laws about life to be discovered which are non-physical by extrapolation from our present concepts. This is nonetheless compatible with there being organizational and functional principles of living systems which are not logical consequences of the organizational and functional principles of non-living physical systems, in the sense that an Apollo rocket is not just a complicated firework. This theme is developed more carefully in the next chapter.

The perception in an object of change with time is dependent upon matching some invariant standard to a changing object as a clock of some kind provides a measure of elapsed time. Unless an invariant standard and a changing object to be assessed are available, there is no use for a clock. Consider how we (as humans) study a relatively closed system. An invariant may be given as a mathematical function and changes determined in the values of various variables of the function by observation or measurement against temporal periods provided by some clock. Other values can then be predicted and tested as a means of checking the appropriateness of the function in providing an invariant standard. In this case, the clock and the system may both be taken as external to the observer, values of both being determined by observation on the part of the observer. In survival, the clock and the invariant as a projected model of reality may both be internal to the observer, with predicted values checked against values determined by perception of the environment, treated as a changing system. One would no more expect that human clocks and human invariants would fit every conceivable set of data than one would expect a carpenter's square of a given size to provide suitable measurements for every undertaking of a carpenter. Similarly, considerations of general relativity theory indicate that an organism's spatio-temporal construction, even as extended by measuring instruments, has a purely limited, as opposed to cosmic, significance.

At a given time in the history of a single individual, the environment of the individual can be taken as a description of its surroundings furnished by another observer, or as a description of these surroundings *as perceived by* the individual. Either of these possibilities raises certain difficulties. If the environment is described by another observer, the individual and its environment are analyzed as separate features of the environment of the observer furnishing the description. This method was originally employed rather naïvely (but understandably) by scientists in order to describe individual members of other species and their environments in an effort to analyze behavior.

The difficulty here is that a describable feature of the individual organism's environment as perceived by a human observer may not be part of the organism's environment in any significant biological sense. If a housefly walks across a proof of Goedel's Theorem, a proof of Goedel's Theorem is not in any significant sense a part of its environment, since the fly could not discriminate between a proof and a typographically similar (there must be some difference) non-proof of the Theorem. One can over-react to this observation by taking the environment of an organism to be given solely by the stimuli which are recognized by the organism's perceptual equipment. But this maneuver causes patent difficulties. For example, an organism may not be able to discriminate between the presence and absence of certain kinds of radiation, even though the radiation may cause certain irreversible chemical processes to take place which could be lethal if the radiation continued long enough. The radiation, causing something to happen to the organism, has to be considered as part of its environment. If we take this seriously, however, we are back into philosophical trouble with the fly. A theorem which it cannot discriminate from a non-theorem (but presumably not Goedel's Theorem) may be used to create an insecticide which eventually proves lethal to the fly, so that the theorem should be taken as part of the animal's environment if causal influence is taken as the defining feature of the environment. Consequently, by trying to find a portion of the universe sufficiently large to enable prediction of the future of a living system, we might have to treat all possible environments of all organisms other than the organism being considered as the environment of the considered organism, a situation which completely paralyzes analysis.

To avoid paralysis, we draw a distinction between the environment of an organism and its perceptual space. We continue to consider the rest of the universe as the environment of an organism, where the environment may well be on a course which will prove fatal to the organism even though the organism cannot forecast its death because it cannot perceive the appropriate cause. On the other hand, the perceptual space of an organism for an observer will be defined as the space of all possible stimulus situations which the organism could discriminate by differential reaction.

We use the term *perception* here quite broadly to say that an organism perceives something if it can react in a relatively short time interval as judged by its own temporal framework to its presence or absence. An organism does not fit its perceptual space exactly. We have said that it fits its environment exactly, but that is a kind of joke following from the way in which the boundary of an organism is to be drawn. To be able to handle and accomplish actual perception, an organism does not change instantaneously when it perceives a new state of its perceptual space. Its ability to predict and control its environment stems from the fact that many different states of its perceptual space can be mapped into the same internal state, or better, mapped into an invariant aspect of its internal state as a relatively decoupled sub-system.

The organism is helpless in an environment which changes too rapidly. To survive, features of the internal model must be made to fit features of the perceived environment in order to satisfy certain internally given requirements. The internal model, on the basis of which courses of action are assessed, is derived by an evolutionary fixation of certain behavioral mechanisms and by the information retained in memory, and it should have (ideally) just the amount of structure required for the anticipated environment. Temporality is involved because the organism can bring about changes in a direction designed to produce coincidence of the internal model with perceived values of the environment. (As with any adjusting mechanism, there may be failures of operation.) In short, the organism is not overwhelmed by its environment, because it has the power to change its environment slightly in an effort to match certain calculated values from its model with perceived values. The organism does not look too far into the future, for values predicted too far in advance would depend upon an influence of the environment which cannot at present be estimated. Again, it does not look too far into the past, for such values are of decreasing significance for current control of perceived values. The relevant information is stored in the generalizations of memory.

Let us consider a human being in a situation where he may

take either of two paths, *A* or *B,* to some desired goal, and let us suppose that these paths are about equal in their demanded effort, and so forth. This situation is quite different from one in which the human being perceives only a single path, say *A.* In the latter case, his expected behavior is quite different from that in the former case. We may say that the available alternative paths to a desired goal are an important determinant of what a human being will do in a given situation.

Curiously, a similar sort of situation exists in microphysics, although with some significant differences. Let a photon be confronted with two paths, *A* and *B,* by which it can reach a screen which will record its arrival, or with a single path *A* obtained from the same experimental arrangement by blocking the path *B.* Under suitable circumstances—the famous two-slit experiment—the expected behavior of the photon will be different in the two cases. (In all such experiments, of course, photons will be emitted from a source which do not reach the screen. A discussion of the experiment rightfully ignores these, for it is only the photons whose paths terminate in the screen that the experiment tells us anything about.) Where two paths exist, the probability of a photon's arrival at a given point on the screen, as verified by the cumulative arrival of single photons on the screen over a long period of time, is almost certainly different from the probability of arrival at the same point on the screen when only the single path exists. (According to the relevant mathematics, a few points will have the same assigned probability.)

If two experimental arrangements are provided, one with two slits, the other quite similar except that one of the slits is blocked, and a source of photons *emitting a single photon at a time* is used to pass photons through the slits of the two arrangements, the screen of the one arrangement will show a pattern completely different from that given on the screen of the other arrangement. Anthropomorphically, we could explain this by saying that the path taken by an individual photon is dependent upon the alternative paths that confront it. Many other features of microphysical events can be phrased in similar anthropomorphic terms. How does a particle obeying an exclusion principle know that it is not in a forbidden state? How does a particle commencing a given orbit know that it is in an acceptable state? We can provide answers if we can imagine, contrary to fact, that the particles could perform sufficient calculations using our physical theories and certain information about their situations.

In the human case, we accept the situation that available choice determines behavior because we can allow the human being to examine the existence of available choices by study of his model for the environment, and we can permit him various computations leading to action based on the processing of this information. In the microphysical case, we cannot readily accept the situation that available choice determines behavior because we are not willing to posit the requisite internal structure to the relevant particle, although some theorists have proposed various ways of positing sub-quantum structure which might eventually provide an explanation of *some* of the observed behavior of microphysical particles. The more typical attitude of physicists is to suppose that quantum-particle behavior must be based on laws of nature quite unlike those involved in classical physics, so much unlike them in fact that classical physics cannot even be regarded as a limiting case of non-classical theories.

There is a mathematical symbolism which will provide correct predictions of the behavior of quantum particles under various familiar experimental conditions. (There are actually several such symbolisms, the use of which must be tailored to circumstances by a kind of art.) The symbolism can be manipulated to yield numbers that can be treated like probabilities. For example, they will yield a number expressing the probability that measurement will locate a given particle at a given point on a screen after a certain elapsed time in a fixed experimental setup. Probabilities of this kind are familiar from classical physics and from ordinary science, but the probabilities involved in microphysics seem to require an interpretation which is unfamiliar in terms of the probabilities which can be computed from classical theories.

Suppose we have a theory which entails the statement that every American owns 1.4 automobiles. Applied to any particular American, the straightforward prediction of this theory is obvious rubbish, since an American can only own a definite, integral number of automobiles. (For simplicity, we will disregard joint ownership, and so forth.) The figure "1.4" is regarded as a weighted sum of the probabilities that an American owns no automobile, owns one automobile, owns two automobiles, and so on. If we look at the records of a particular American, we may observe, for example, that he owns exactly two automobiles. We would assume that this observation simply revealed a determinate state of affairs which existed before the observation. A key difference between classical observation or measurement and microphysical measurement is that there are sound reasons for denying that quantum systems are similarly in determinate states before measurement of them reveals a value of some kind.

To see what this involves, we can return to the two-slit experiment. On the human analogy, the human can accumulate information, make a decision, and then pursue a chosen path. Once he starts out on this path, however, if the other path were closed, it would make no difference to his behavior. (If he knew the second path were closed, he might be more anxious about his journey, but we can dismiss these complications in our example.) But the actual data of the quantum experiment, the path of the photon *is* sensitive to the existence or non-existence of both slits. We can't split the photon up and send a part through each slit (it is theoretically indivisible) in order to explain this sensitivity, and we can't have the photon passing through a single slit without being baffled by its sensitivity to the opening of the other slit. The conclusion forced on us by classical logic is that the photon passes through neither slit, and hence does not have a determinate location or state at all times between its emission and its termination in the screen. The conclusion seems plainly absurd, but it has been forced upon physicists by the cumulative record of microphysical experimentation. To circumvent the absurdity of the conclusion we must give up various notions of causality or temporality at the quantum level (easily conceived, but difficult to work out in any detail) or we must suppose that a photon has features completely unlike those of any classical particle or wave.

This last suppostion can in turn be handled in two ways. One might suppose that classical particles and waves have hitherto unnoticed features—unnoticed because they lie below a certain threshold of measurement which microphysical theory has revealed—*or* we can suppose that the features of the quantum particles when not measured are simply not determinate in any sense familiar from classical physics. The majority of physicists seem to have adopted some version of this latter view, a view which has sometimes been characterized by philosophers as a vicious form of operationism. On philosophically operationist principles, although a diamond is hard whenever it is subjected to a scratch test, it might be as soft as buttermilk in between tests (compatibly with the logic of the situation). To avoid this absurdity, the logician requires some principle of uniformity of nature as an additional premise. The scientist would more likely be interested to know what force would cause the change in the properties of the diamond in such intervals. This reasonable view which may conceal an implicit metaphysical attitude is entirely suitable in classical physics, where the measurement process can be regarded as leaving relevant physical properties invariant. But in microphysical measurement, there are many reasons for supposing that measured properties may be properties created by the measuring apparatus.

Once again, microphysical measurement bears similarities to biological measurement that it does not bear to classical measurement. Natives interrogated by anthropologists or sociologists are sometimes thought to irreversibly change characteristics faster than an accurate picture of their aboriginal state can be assimilated from the interviews. Microphysical measurement gives the same sort of frustration, except at a more irritative level. Whereas both the diamond and the native are supposed to be in some determinate state at a certain time prior to measured results, the photon in transition, and other microphysical particles during certain intervals, seems to have no determinate state at all during such intervals, so that the microphysical picture is not simply an historical repetition of an earlier operationism (or positivism) held by some scientists and philosophers with respect to classical theories.

The problem of measurement in microphysical theory is a fascinating challenge for philosophical scientists, and there is a voluminous technical literature exploring rival approaches to explaining the significance of measurement. Although no very coherent account of these controversies is possible here, the existence of the difficulty is not unrelated to our major themes.

First, consider the more or less orthodox opinion just discussed that quantum physical systems have no determinate state in intervals between measurements. Now suppose we have a quantum system involving a photon which, according to theory, may with roughly equal probability take either of two paths *A* or *B* to two different screens. The photon hitting the screen can cause an irreversible chemical change which can be amplified so as to result in a definite macroscopic event. In a famous example—Schroedinger's Cat—a photon either passes or does not pass through a half-silvered mirror, causing the death of a cat by gunshot or electrocution only if it passes through the mirror. This is, at any rate, our classical interpretation of a piece of apparatus containing a live cat at the present time. Quantum theory is apparently broad enough in scope to provide an explanation of the development in time of the photon plus the apparatus as a closed system. At a time when it is known that a photon has either passed or not passed through the mirror, common sense would dictate that the cat was either dead or not dead, depending on the particular path taken by the photon through the apparatus. But by quantum theoretical law on the orthodox interpretation, the *indeterminateness* of the photon's path (similar to that of the two-slit experiment) is linked to an indeterminateness of the entire system, and the cat is neither dead nor not dead but is in a state which can be described as a *superposition* of these two states.

The failure of classical logic to describe the situation follows from the interpretation in which it is not permitted to say that one state obtains, *although* we do not *know* which. Now let a human being look into the apparatus and ascertain that the cat is dead or that it isn't. This measurement resolves the situation, and given the intended absurdity of the example, it may be said to show that on the orthodox theory the observer has killed the cat (if it is dead) by looking at it. The real curiosity of the situation comes in exactly at this point if it is compatible (as it is usually thought) with orthodox quantum theory to say that the cat is definitely dead or not dead after a suitable measurement. Quantum theory can consider the photon plus the apparatus plus the human organism as an even larger closed quantum system. But again, the quantum theoretical description is incompatible with saying that the cat, or the human organism, is in some definite state at the time of the measurement. In order to account for the appearance of a definite state, the orthodox interpretation then depends upon introducing the observer's consciousness which has the physically *sui generis* ability to *determine its own state*. The determinateness of the state of the cat and the retrospective path of the photon then can be deduced because of the quantum theoretical link of the human organism to the rest of the system.

The philosophical difficulty is that the ability of the consciousness of the observer to determine its own state has no theoretical explanation in terms of the theory. This difficulty, among others, is responsible for the considerable activity directed at finding other explanations of quantum measurement that will not have this awkward consequence. (See Further Reading, at the end of this book, for some suggestions about the details.) Most of the alternatives to the theory just sketched include a supposition, not justified by quantum theory in its usual formulation, that at least certain macro-observables keep sharp values at all times, a supposition which will allow measurement to be represented in the example by letting the state of the apparatus after passage of the photon have a definite value. These variations remain incomplete in the sense that the mechanisms in macro-objects which would account for continuous sharp values of observables are no clearer than the postulated abilities of mind to determine its own state. There is consequently no justification for considering either micro-phenomena or macro-phenomena more fundamental, and above all no reduction of one to the other.

We have therefore reached this point: if one traces physical theory to its roots by following a widely accepted account of measurement in quantum theory, the explicit appearance of mind cannot be eliminated. The alternatives require a sharp distinction between two kinds of observables, so that important features of classical theories remain in any complete characterization of physical theory. Neither of these results need bother physicists who pursue no reductionist program, but as we will see in the next chapter, it is an embarrassing subject for philosophers who pursue reductionist schemes in which an important desideratum is the reduction of mental phenomena to some kind of fundamental physical principles. The thrust of more generalized reductionist programs is almost completely blunted, if it is true, as has been suggested in this chapter, that irreversible classical processes are not eliminable from any full description of physical theory.

7

Life

In its simplest form, the adoption of physics as the sole paradigm of sound scientific practice amounts to the suggestion that all scientific knowledge can be explained solely in terms of physical laws. In one sense such a claim is trivially true in a manner which is not intended by philosophers who suppose that in this manner all scientific knowledge can be reduced to physics and lawful extensions of physical principles. It has been suggested that the word *physical* is used coincidentally with the range of what we think we can fully understand. Should we have an agreed upon explanation of some natural phenomenon, it simply comes to be known as a physical explanation. This linguistic observation is related to the role that physics has played within the structure of institutionalized science, but the observation is likely to remain true for a future in which scientific practice as we know it remains an important feature of society.

The truth of the trivial reducibility claim can be clearly exhibited in scientific history. It is hard to imagine how peculiar the early observation of electromagnetic phenomena must have seemed to scientists who were familiar only with forces acting on a line connecting two visible bodies or particles. But the explanations of these new phenomena were absorbed into the range of physical explanations as a formalism was developed which fitted the astonishing new facts. Electromagnetic theory cannot be reduced in any clear sense to the physical theories which preceded it. Many of the electromagnetic laws cannot be expressed in terms of the mathematics of earlier systems in any perspicuous fashion, and electromagnetic radiation cannot be analyzed into particles and forces along the lines of classical mechanics. The electromagnetic phenomena were emergent by comparison to earlier physics, but their scientific and objective status became clarified by absorption into an expanded physical theory.

These observations about a trivial interpretation of the reductionist argument rest on a sense of *physical* which is nearly coincident in meaning with *natural* or *scientific*. To put bite into a claim about reduction, *physical* must be taken to suggest something more closely associated with the laws of physics current at the time when the reductionist argument is advanced. The development of new theories like that required historically for explanation of electromagnetic phenomena must be regarded in retrospect as a technical justification of some of the features of non-reductionist opinion advanced at earlier times. If we expect new phenomena to arise as physics is developed, an expectation well supported by the history of physics, we should be wary of advancing strong reductionist claims going beyond the trivial reading already noted.

Except for the sheer love of controversy, there is very little reason to argue over whether various processes in living organisms, for example, will ultimately receive an explanation in terms of currently known physical laws. They simply might or they might not. If a guess had to be made, however, the existence of difficulties with the notion of measurement, and the obvious signs pointing toward organizational principles in the structure of living matter not found in simple molecules would suggest that there are probably some profound discoveries to be made before physical theory can provide a reasonable explanation of the gross features of biological organisms.

Why can't we decide definitely whether or not various processes occurring in living organisms are surprising, as were those observed in early stages of electromagnetic or quantum discovery, and that these phenomena will thus require augmentation of the stock of physical laws? In the cited cases of past surprising physical phenomena, experiments showing the phenomena were usually performed in early stages of research on objects and forces which were already thought to be comprehensible in terms of an existing theory. In physics, when an anomalous phenomenon was repeatedly observed, it was then clear that the known laws were insufficient to account for it. On the contrary, in biology no one has an understanding of relevant life processes extensive enough to detect anomalies in experimentation.

The philosophical literature contains a number of purported models for reduction which have been used to explain strong reductionist proposals to the effect that theories other than those of physics should be reduced to physical theories if they are to have full scientific status in terms of the requirements of some logical model. The details of these models are not important, particularly since they usually assume that theories are given as axiomatic systems.

Let it be proposed that one theory T_1 be reduced to another theory T_2. In our case, we assume that T_2 is either a theory of physics or a theory which is independently reducible to physics. T_1 will contain some vocabulary not in the vocabulary of T_2. We assume that correlations can be established, for example, definitions, giving the vocabulary of T_1 an interpretation in terms of the vocabulary of T_2. The usual method is to provide a definition of each term occurring in T_1 by means of a logical function involving the vocabulary of T_2. Then consider any true statement of T_1, or any theorem of T_1 if T_1 is expressed as an axiomatic system. When its vocabulary is replaced by the means of the definitions with the correlated logical function involving vocabulary of T_2, the result must be a true sentence of T_2.

It is extremely doubtful that *any* reduction has ever taken place along such lines in the history of science, or whether such reductions could even be carried out in detail for the cases of reduction most often alluded to. The case of reduction in science most often referred to in support of reductionist proposals is that of phenomenological thermodynamics to a form of statistical mechanics, but in this reduction, certain of the phenomenological statements which express temporal directedness in the phenomenological theory go over into correlated statements which are temporally isotropic or undirected. Irreversibility on the phenomenological level becomes reversibility (in theory) on the reduced level. Consequently, the reduced theory appears to be incompatible with the reducing theory. Removal of the incompatibility depends upon adding assumptions about various parameters of particular systems which cannot be taken as reductions of any statements in the phenomenological theory, and which are certainly not laws of the reducing theory. In a typical case, generalizations in the reducing theory may be seen as intuitively equivalent to generalizations in the reduced theory only if the systems studied have a sufficient number of particles, and satisfy various other requirements that cannot be stated in the reduced theory. In general, successful reduction of biological or chemical theory to some physical theory seems to require some alteration in the reduced theory.

The role of reduction in science, in view of this fact, is probably simply to establish that the higher-level theory need involve no reference to strange or unusual mechanisms in its statement and development. The reduction of thermodynamics, for example, is intended to show that heat phenomena need not be explained and are not conceptually dependent upon any notion of a caloric fluid, but could be explained in terms of other well-understood mechanisms occurring elsewhere in physics. Strictly, the reduction involves two logically incompatible theories. To say that two theories are incompatible is to say that there are statements following from each which appear to contain the same vocabulary, and which are inconsistent on the assumption that the vocabulary is the same. What the discussions of the reduction show is that these two theories will give nearly identical results in various similar cases when they are correctly used to state the cases, but the techniques for providing a correct theoretical description of a similar case in each theory are part of its intelligent use, and not part of its apparent formalism.

On reductionist views, a theory is usually regarded as a static structure, a fact that is nearly obvious when definitions of the reducing relation are given only for cases where the two theories involved can be represented as axiomatic systems. The success of a reductionist program then shows us what the elements of the reduced structure are composed of. It's rather like having a shape covered with tissue paper and then stripping the paper away to see what the structure has been composed of. But this process can be carried so far, and no further, for when analysis is made fine enough, there may be no specialized parts making up the structure. It would be like saying that a successful definition of a human being should be able to lead to a determination of whether any specific electron, for example, was part of the organism or part of the environment. If specific parts at some level of analysis may be omitted or changed without structural alteration, analysis has clearly carried beyond the level of explanation. It is not necessary nor even useful that explanation of how something works be carried to interactions of the smallest conceivable entities within the boundaries of the object. For example, we can understand the workings of a clock in terms of the parts which are manufactured and placed into its mechanism, along with a description of its mechanism in classical terms. The feeling that the clock's working can be understood in these terms seems entirely justified.

If omission of a part causes a machine to fail in its operation, we can justify our claim that the part is essential. A similar explanation can be provided for various deformations of the part. When we build or construct a machine that successfully accomplishes some task, we have a straightforward observation of its success and a straightforward explanation of that success in terms of its parts. The material making up the parts is often irrelevant. A machine accomplishing a certain task could be manufactured out of various kinds of metals, or out of metals in some cases and plastics in another, and have its workings explained in each case by the same principles. Because of this fact, the discovery of new machines always seems to provide explanations of behavior in all sorts of unexpected places. The discovery of self-regulating, self-adapting, and self-reproducing machines has provided a wealth of explanation of how various biological processes might operate and be controlled.

Compare this to the attempted analysis of a machine of unknown function. (Just how something can be recognized as a machine if its function is unknown would probably not be soluble in the general case, but there is an archaeology of machines based on reasonable analogies between the shape of parts of known machines and those of discovered objects.) To take a simple illustration, it may not be possible to determine whether two pieces of an unknown machine are actually two parts of the machine, or two pieces of a broken part, or a part and an odd bit from something else, or two separate machines, and so on.

In general, explanation of a machine's working depends upon an analysis of the function of the machine. No one has ever shown how the workings of a simple machine used by human being can be deduced from the laws of the molecules which happen to compose it. The correct working of an ordinary machine is suitably described in terms of the parts which compose it and a classical description of their interaction. Two clocks which differ in their time keeping in similar circumstances but which are built according to the same plan will both completely satisfy the laws of physics. The difference in their rate can no doubt be found in some physical difference which can be described, but which is not a matter of physical law. They may have been fitted with some part of slightly different shape due to variations in the manufacturing. This difference cannot follow from the laws of physics unless one takes a position that the position of each part of the universe is determinable by physical laws from the beginning of physical time, a view which is an entirely gratuitous expression of a philosophical metaphysics hardly supported by scientific practice.

It is well known that the adequacy of classical physics in explaining the operation of machines at the unaided human level of observation is compatible with an indeterministic microphysics at a level of observation determined by accelerators, and so on. This compatibility is difficult to work out on a reductionist model. We have previously indicated that there are logical incompatibilities between microphysics, in any of its usual formulations, and classical physical theory. Although microphysics utilizes a basically deterministic mathematical theory, the important restriction on this observation is that the mathematical theory can provide a description only for closed systems of an appropriate kind. Closed microphysical systems are typically indeterminate when they are opened during the measurement process, and microphysical systems of a complexity corresponding to classical structures are so complex that at any current levels of integrating theory, no successful predictions of their future states are possible which do not rely on the help of some classical discoveries and observations. Nevertheless, microphysical theory can provide some understanding of classical structures (like a clock mechanism) not provided by classical theory or by a description of its macroscopic parts and their function. A microphysical theory can explain the incorrect working of a clock under non-optimal conditions, that is, why it must eventually fail to keep time correctly and why it will no longer keep time as correctly if it is heated. (In this situation, we don't apply enough heat to destroy the macroscopic identity of the parts, of course, since failure consequent upon that is also explained by classical theory.) The compatibility between classical theory and microphysical theory is demonstrated in this case by showing that the clock at room temperature operates nearly as it would at absolute zero, where microphysical indeterminism can be overlooked. As in the case of the reduction of phenomonological thermodynamics to statistical mechanics, the theories are incompatible, but they will yield nearly identical results in certain similar cases where they are correctly used to describe the situation.

The important observation is that it would not be correct

to say that the clock was not understood until the microphysical theory appeared. Microphysical theory was not developed to fit a data environment whose features were determined by ordinary clock mechanisms. As in the case of our biological example, microphysical theory explains the similarities between machines, but not the difference that we are interested in, which have to be explained by more classical theories and which may ultimately rest on specific structural differences that cannot be deduced from any scientific laws.

Can we provide a reasonable account of how one theory is reduced to another as this relationship is exhibited in scientific practice rather than as it is interpreted in some philosophical program? To understand the relationship, we need to compare the environments of instances of various theories. In Capter Four we interpreted theories as being adaptive mechanisms for dealing with data environments. Now, a particular instance of a theory may be viable in a very small, although extremely complicated, environment. Consider a classical gas law describing accurately enough the behavior of a particular sample of a gas in a particular cylinder under certain definite circumstances. Here, measurement of two gross features is sufficient to explain and predict various other measurements of the same features. The well-known inverse relationship between pressure and volume at constant temperature for a suitable gas provides a convenient example.

A measurement of the pressure and volume at one time along with a measurement of the volume at a later time enables us to calculate the pressure at the later time. One instantiation of the classical theory thus provides a great deal of information about the behavior of the gas. The reducing theories, either statistical or microphysical depending on the level, do not provide a function such that the gross features of the behavior of the gas can be predicted by substitution of a finite number of values for variables of the function. The reducing theories can have an exact instantiation only for very small sub-systems of the gas, consisting of a few molecules which can be treated as closed, so that the gross features given by the classical theory and macroscopic measurement must be regarded as reached by some kind of limiting process which transcends the exact mathematical treatment of a closed sub-system of the gas being considered. The passage from the treatment in the reducing theory of sub-systems to predictions about the total system must be made by intuition, or perhaps by exact mathematical techniques at least as powerful as those used in the analytical integration of real functions. This is not to suggest that passage to these predictions cannot be made rigorous, but that it simply does not fit the detailed requirements of philosophical models of reduction. Philosophical models typically depend on analyzing a statement into a logical function of simpler statements. Limiting processes usually transcend the logical functions of repeated conjunction and quantification allowed in the models.

It is possible to analyze a static structure into parts and their features such that all of the information about the macro-object is contained in the description of the parts and their features, even though the features of the macro-object cannot be deduced from the features of the micro-description. An idealized example is furnished by Zeno's paradox of length. A line segment of unit length consists of nothing but points, each of which has length zero. The length of the line segment cannot be determined from the lengths of its constituent points even by infinite conjunction. To obtain the length of the segment from the lengths of the points requires integration, a technique more powerful than any technique of formal logic embodied in the reduction models. Techniques of integration can be formalized as axiomatic theories within the logical systems, but they depend upon non-empirical existence theorems which capture a mathematical intuition about various limiting processes. Thus the macroscopic regularities cannot in interesting and significant cases be *deduced* by logical derivation from instantiations of the underlying micro-theory.

It would be contended by many philosophers that the problem for reduction suggested in the last paragraph cannot strictly appear in actual physical circumstances because of the finitude of the relevant elements of a physical system. Nonetheless, if we take microphysical theory into account, we have a closely related problem. Instead of an infinitude of elements with exact properties (in particular, exact locations), we have a large finitude of elements possessing inexact properties. This situation seems even more desperate. In other words, we now have to explain how the physical system can be so closely described by classical laws although it could not make accurate computations from the properties of its smallest parts. Now some physical systems are no doubt unstable in the face of slight changes in microphysical parameters, but systems accurately described by classical laws, as well as living organisms, seem stable in the face of considerable microphysical fluctuation in their sub-systems.

So far, we have been discussing the philosophical problem of life from a rather oblique angle. The point is this. At present, biological knowledge is not reducible to known physical laws. If reductionism is accepted in any strong form, there is no interesting philosophical problem. There is only experimentation and scientific work to be done. But if the considerations of the last two chapters are sound, and we will assume here that they are, we have an interesting philosophical problem about levels of organization which arises within the domain of physical knowledge. The problem is to define the possibility and hopefully explain how a system may operate in close conformance with classical laws if it is composed of particles not operating in conformance with these laws.

We cannot suppose that the behavior of macro-systems is self-determined somehow by a process which can be described as the computation of values of various functions somewhat in the manner that a human scientist effects prediction. The facts suggest rather that our theories describe the behavior of various systems without providing any insight into how the systems themselves have their behavior determined. A reasonable suggestion would be that the behavior of at least some physical systems is affected only by the system's determination of relatively gross changes in its underlying physical structure, much as human behavior may be motivated by relatively gross bodily changes that are in turn insensitive to wide ranges of molecular fluctuation, at least in normal circumstances.

Should such a situation be possible, one could expect levels of analysis of our environment not reducible by law one to the other and such that deterministic levels would have indeterministic levels underneath them, and so forth. It is clear from the discussion of the clock how a deterministic level of explanation might, at one level of analysis, have an indeterministic microphysical level constituting its sub-systems. A part of such a deterministic device can be considered an effectively closed system with respect to some function, in that it retains a certain invariance in spite of energy fluctuations across its boundary, If we were to open the system represented by such a part and look at some small enough part of the part, so to speak, our opening of the system might necessarily cause the part to be sensitive to the overwhelming effect of its environment, and effect which might force us to treat the part indeterministically because of uncertainty in our calculations—perhaps because of the failure of our concepts to apply at this level, and perhaps because of indeterminateness in whatever determines the physical processes. Its motions within the functioning part of the mechanism from which it is taken may be determined by a macroscopic structure which can no longer be seen at this level.

To complete a levels picture, it would also be necessary to indicate how an indeterministic level could have a deterministic level under it. One standard version of this situation requires that the indeterministic level be provided by a kind of ignorance of the underlying deterministic level so that irreducibility cannot ultimately be defended. For example, a penny tossed from an appropriate mechanism onto a surface seems to provide an indeterministic phenomenon over a period of time, but it can be argued that the indeterminism is due simply to our failure to determine precisely enough the initial or boundary conditions just prior to each toss. This situation is not correctly describable as existing on two levels, since it is really being argued in this kind of use of the example that the indeterministic level can be theoretically reduced to the deterministic level. Now, in the situation which can make sense given current physical theory, a deterministic level is separated from an indeterministic level because measurements on the deterministic level are insensitive to a wide class of indeterministic fluctuations on the micro-level. The problem is then to find how an indeterministic level may be constructed which is not reducible to a deterministic level if an ontology of the distinct levels is to be defended.

Consider a deterministic mechanism which can be in a number of states, including a state in which one of two paths is chosen by amplifying the outcome of some indeterministic phenomenon from a lower level. Such a mechanism would be, in a sense, neither deterministic nor indeterministic, since the predictability of its behavior from a fixed starting point would depend upon whether the state effecting an indeterministic decision between alternatives was switched on during the relevant temporal interval. In the general case, however, the theory of the mechanism would have to be regarded as indeterministic if there were starting points from which it could be shown that the indeterministic state would be reached. The behavior of such a mechanism could always be explained in retrospect, for we might be able to determine that the indeterministic program had been utilized to select a path of behavior, and that it has operated in such and such a manner. The indeterministic phenomenon used in a *randomizing state* (a term we will use hereafter to refer to such a selection state) need not be at any particular level, it need only occur at a level on which the ordinary measuring devices of the mechanism are insensitive to wide fluctuations. To return to the penny, it is possible to conceive that there are states discriminable by some measuring apparatus in the naturally occurring organism. There may be such states corresponding to initial starting positions, which are *not* discriminable by a man tossing a penny from his hand. Then the penny's behavior in being tossed from the hand is indeterministic at the human level.

Now the outcome of a toss of a penny is not relevant (save

in bizarre fictional circumstances which we can ignore) to a path taken by human behavior unless some human *chooses* to use a toss of a penny as a randomizing state, albeit an external one. In this sense, a human coupled to a tossed penny is an irreducibly indeterministic system with respect to some levels of analysis, even though we can regard its behavior as that exhibited by an (indeterministic) mechanism because we can understand how the system operates.

The *metaphysical view* being suggested here is that one can imagine an indeterministic substratum on which deterministic levels are constructed. Further, indeterministic levels may be sandwiched between the deterministic levels by the ability of the deterministic levels to contain mechanisms which can amplify and use changes of state at a lower level (changes it cannot predict by a prior use of its measuring devices) to construct randomizing states. This view, which I will call *indeterministic mechanism,* is closely tied to the development of an adequate theory of measurement permitting measurement of micro-physical states to take place in the absence of the human mind.

Indeterministic mechanism has the interesting consequence that randomizing states may be required for the successful operation of mechanisms of a certain level of complexity. It could be necessary for the continued operation of a mechanism that it pass into some determinate state within a certain period of time whenever it is confronted with alternative paths of behavior. Now suppose that a mechanism, although its measuring devices were normally insensitive to wide fluctuations of state on some underlying level, attained a state where two measuring devices (possibly in a redundant circuit) which nearly always gave the same measurement and forced the same next state, produced measured values which were indicative of different future states for the organism to assume. The mechanism (like Buridan's Ass) might be stymied except for the presence of a randomizing state which it might utilize on the grounds that transformation into either of the indicated next states would be preferable to continued indecision.

Suppose it is accepted that as matters stand, we can agree

to the possibility of the existence of levels of physical explanation, some deterministic and some indeterministic, and that reduction of explanations on these levels to some fundamental physical theory on a philosophical model is not possible. The philosophical reductionist would not be prepared to accept this description on the grounds that its existence could show at most that there were alternative possibilities, and not that his position is wrong. A crucial reason why the reductionist may prefer to keep his view without discussing the likelihoods of alternatives is that he is dominated by an historical picture which seems to coerce his attention away from a discussion of the likelihood of rival views which are grounded in any assessment of the relevance of current physical theory to some ideal reductionist account. This historical picture suggests that if we could construct a film of the history of the universe we would have to show it first without definite physical objects, then with definite physical objects but no living organisms, then with physical objects and living organisms but no human organisms before finally arriving at a picture of the current situation. Further, the reductionist might argue that this account alone is compatible with the major threads of our picture of the universe as portrayed in generalized science.

It would thus seem that the current distinction between living and non-living systems must have originated lawfully from a universe in which there were no living systems. This picture is almost certainly a vestige of a metaphysical view not consistent with current scientific views, and one which hardly exhausts the logical possibilities. The reductionist position is closely tied to the picture offered in this film, for any alternative which supposes that mental phenomena are present in all matter (mental forces which are even weaker then gravitational forces in small systems) is an alternative which is non-reductionistic on the very simple grounds that it must predict quite new physical phenomena and physical laws to be discovered in the future. And views which posit that living systems have always existed in the universe, or that there are non-reducible levels of organization which may evolve over time in an indeterministic universe, are clearly incompatible with the picture suggested by the reductionist.

Suppose we grant the reductionist view which is suggested. The primary challenge to be opposed to it here—a challenge which may eventually show decisively the small likelihood of the reductionist view—is that the reductionist view is inconsistent with any reasonable explanation of the observable gross features of evolutionary development, both of living and non-living systems.

Any detailed discussion of reductionism must take into account a definite cosmological theory. To simplify somewhat, we would have to accept some cosmological theory which is consistent with the film of the history of the universe suggested. This means that steady-state cosmologies are left standing, for in a steady-state cosmology, there is no logical reason why life should disappear from the universe as one extrapolates backward in time. A basic postulate of steady-state cosmologies is that the cosmological features of the universe (these *might* not include living systems) are invariant over time. Consequently the steady-state cosmology does not seem a suitable background for the events in our film. Let us then take an evolutionary or cyclic view on which the current state of the universe is to be regarded as a consequence of some state in which the universe is represented as a collection of particles whose behavior is fully accounted for by laws at a fundamental reducing level. A very important difficulty is to imagine how any reasonable constraints can be applied to this state in order to see how a later determinate state of the universe can be reached by deterministic law. A very early state would probably escape deterministic description in terms of spatio-temporal parameters. To avoid a consequent early demise for the reductionist view, we have to consider a later state which can suitably be described on the film.

If this state is fully describable by the laws of microphysics along the lines that can currently be anticipated, then there is the considerable problem of how the system could develop a series of determinate states that could be shown on the film.

In other words, the film would seem to have a number of different possible beginnings compatible with the fixed later state. A universe would have to be extremely sensitive to microphysical fluctuation as soon as systems capable of measurement evolved. As we extrapolate backward, we reach a point where our film-making is pure fantasy.

A similar consequence seems to hold if the fundamental theory is a statistical but deterministic theory with properties like those of statistical mechanics. The point is that the constraints governing predictable development of macroscopic systems interacting with other systems, such as the constraints imposed by a suitable container (which has solid walls on the micro-level) on the development of an equilibrium state in a contained gas, are simply not represented by any structure in the postulated primitive state (where there are no walls). It is simply not clear how an evolution consisting of a series of determinate states can proceed without some measurement process and macroscopic structure which is insensitive to wide fluctuations in underlying microstates, and which hence constitutes a deterministic level of analysis of the system. A postulated state of the universe early enough in a film of the history of the universe would seem to allow no scope for the existence of the relevant macroscopic structures.

On the other hand, if we were to allow indeterminism at a fundamental level, it is at least conceivable, although no theory of evolution is available at present to explain all of the details, that macroscopic, deterministic structures might have occasionally formed as relatively closed structures within an indeterministically evolving universe. The basis for the intelligibility of this view lies in the simple observation that stable structures can evolve in an array of randomly shaken parts which can become linked together by specially fitted surfaces which are held by strong magnetic or spring-loaded forces once they happen to encounter each other. At another level, significant expressions can be located by random play among various elements, an idea intelligible enough that some theories of concept formation are based on (random) trial-and-error play with previously formed conceptual bits. Of course, once macroscopic deterministic structures happen to appear, it is easily conceivable how they can place important constraints on other systems. Once we have a man, it is easy to see how he can impose various orders on relevantly unstructured material to create new deterministic mechanisms. *The basic metaphysical idea is this:* it is conceivable that order (and trivially, disorder) can be obtained from disorder, but not conceivable how disorder can be obtained from order, except in the sense of an entropy increase. There is thus some warrant for accepting a level of analysis of structures along the general lines that have been indicated, with indeterminism expected to be marked at very fundamental levels.

What is then required is to show that at least two different, irreducible levels are possible. A short answer is to say that we have already seen them exhibited in a mechanism like a clock. The long answer is to raise our challenge to reductionism again by pointing out that various features of any suggested evolutionary development of living organisms seems best explicable by reference to such irreducible levels. For example, the basic process of sexual reproduction in determining the inheritance of offspring seems related to a suitably deterministic process of construction of the features of a phenotype from the features of a randomly chosen genotype. In other words, the development of a particular organism from a fertilized egg seems certainly to follow various deterministic constraints. Very briefly, we don't get lions from acorns. But the nature of the genotype embodied in the egg seems certainly determined by an indeterministic process.

If inheritance was explainable in terms of a determination by law, one would expect the members of species to gradually show increasingly identical genotypes in the face of selection pressure from a fixed environment. The observed maintenance of a gene pool through various mechanisms, represented by the highly variable genotypes of individual members of a species, seems to depend essentially on random selection of genotypes, a selection which can be isolated from the control of parent organisms. If this levels picture is correct, the gross features of reproductive mechanisms seem intelligible; if not, they seem very difficult to explain. Acceptance of the reductionist program thus seems to entail that very plain facts consistent with various other views must receive a dubious interpretation, based on a promissory note of lengthy expected maturity, which anticipates developments in scientific theory not currently even on the horizon.

The levels picture has been objected to in that no purely random processes could exist in nature, because the notion of a purely random sequence is mathematically intractable. All that the levels picture requires for the existence of randomizing states, in particular for the randomizing states of living organisms, is that there exist processes at *lower* levels comparable to that of various mechanisms at the *higher* level the outcome of which can be discerned but not predicted from initial conditions as discerned by the measuring devices. These processes need not exhibit outcomes showing mathematical randomness. The necessity of levels can be preserved if an organism which solves the prediction problem for some lower-level process by development of its measuring systems can find another process to serve as the basis for its randomizing states. This kind of change is quite compatible with evolutionary theory, provided that randomizing states are required, along with determined states, for the existence of life. The whole tenor of our suggestions has been that at the level of living organisms a structure has developed which is more complex than that exhibited by non-living organisms in the same fashion that the structure of a digital computer is more complex than the structure of a simple mechanical clock, and certainly irreducible to a structure whose elements are structures of the latter kind. Such a structure from a theoretical viewpoint is a complex of random and deterministic states designed to solve certain problems of maintaining important invariances or maximizing certain functions. Both levels of state must apparently exist simultaneously in the same organization.

It's interesting to look at certain problems about the human mind from this standpoint. It may well be that lower organisms have evolved a complex of reflex (deterministic) patterns of response to certain perceptions, and of random (startle, panic) patterns of response to certain other perceptions. We could regard these various patterns as independent programs used to assess the input of certain perceptual mechanisms in a more central nervous system. A living organism of any complexity (judged at the level of biological organization) would apparently need to solve a problem which would be raised by situations in which these genetically embedded programs produced contradictory results, and this problem obviously requires some high-level adaptive program if successful assessment of the lower-level outputs is to be undertaken. Mere random selection of response would not require a hierarchical structure. What is required for selection is in fact a mechanism for determining the response of the organism, where possible, when lower-level programs conflict, much as a mathematician would try to locate and remove by rational methods the source of difficulty in an inconsistent axiomatic system, although he could simply try some random change in the axioms. The difficulty with randomized change is its low survival value: the wrong guess is fatal, and there are typically many alternative choices of response. So randomizing states would not be deliberately invoked by a living organism except to resolve a situation which could not be deterministically resolved because the alternatives seemed either incommensurable or identical when inspected by higher-level programs.

Consciousness may well be a symptom of such a higher-level program in higher organisms whose lower-level programs may issue contradictory outputs. Typically, the activities of consciousness would be deterministic, but a consciousness could resolve various situations by choosing to activate a random state. Consciousness would thus probably appear as a result of a distinct and novel structural organization of brains in higher organisms, but it would not reflect a structure easily described as either deterministic or indeterministic because of the possibility of its determined use of randomizing states. At this level of complexity, simple arguments about determinism and indeterminism would lose their point. In the human case, we could see how behavior might be unpredictable because of random states, even though the will and consciousness would be aspects of a mechanism usually proceeding by deterministic steps on the basis of a measurement process resulting in determinate values for various sub-systems of the organism.

We can now attempt some *summary* of the major consequences of the evolutionary viewpoint which has been developed in this book. As the last two chapters have attempted to make clear, the evolutionary viewpoint is not only compatible with, but potentially explanatory of, a view of scientific theories which contends that some theories exist on irreducible levels of analysis with respect to other theories, although the former are not autonomous of the latter in the sense that the shape of the data environment, plus various criteria of viability, place strong objective constraints on their structures. The evolutionary view is also not only compatible with, but explanatory of, the patent fact that alternative theories are required for sound scientific knowledge, and for coherent progress in fitting new data environments. When these consequences arc weighed, it would seem reasonable to conclude that no view holding that there is a single sound logical structure to be found in adequate representations of good scientific theories (and which can be traced in the outlines of some fundamental physical theory) is tenable in the face of the diverse record of sound scientific practice to be distilled from the relevant history.

The evolutionary view is equally fatal to any strong claims about the methodological unity of scientific practice which contend that there is a single logical pattern describing the relationship between theory and experimental data. As organisms show different patterns of adaptation to selection pressure from their environments, we may also expect various theories to be related in relatively unusual ways to their data environments in the face of the unique characteristics of certain environments. Suppose that one has a theory according to which some set of objects are all identical. Call such a set of objects a *homogeneous class*. A successful methodology for investigation of these objects is perfectly simple, at least in retrospect. The homogeneous class is sampled by observing or measuring a few objects from the class—choosing a sample large enough to swamp the effects of experimental error, if possible—in order to determine certain characteristics. It is then entirely reasonable to project regularities based on such observation or measurements over the rest of the homogeneous class. For example, it is assumed in physical theory that all electrons are identical. In measuring the charge of one electron, therefore, one has measured the charge of all electrons. The interplay between observation and assumption is more complex than this suggests, but it seems clear that the theories of physics have dealt largely with homogeneous classes, and have proposed theories by projection of characteristics over such classes on the basis of an assumed theoretical identity.

By contrast to the theories of physics, the theories of biology have had to deal rather with non-homogeneous, or *heterogeneous,* classes. Suppose we adopt the common view that the cell is a minimal part of most biological organisms. (This is not to say that biological organization may not appear in lower levels, for example in enzymatically controlled chemical reactions, but that the behavior of living organisms may be explained in terms of cellular behavior as a terminal structural order in many cases.) According to biological theory, any two cells containing different nuclear or cytoplasmic structure will be different, and *any* two cells, even with the same structure, will become sharply discriminable in behavior in certain circumstances due to biographical differences embedded in memory. Therefore, biological theory provides no warrant for projection of generalizations from the study of certain cells to all cells or to wide classes of cells on any assumption of theoretical identity.

In the rare cases where homogeneous classes exist in biology, for example, pure strains in classical genetics, the methodology of projection by generalization seems adequate. But the fact that increasing complexity on even a theoretical level may mean that the methodology appropriate for homogeneous classes must be replaced by other techniques, perhaps akin to some from of gestalt perception as well as other devices in sciences dealing with heterogeneous classes, should suggest to philosophers of science that views holding that a single logical model for the relationship of theory to data is sufficient for a philosophically useful account of scientific practice are probably a gross oversimplification. This position is supported by considerable evidence of a somewhat subtle cast, such as the failure to date of attempts to predict the actions of single human organisms based on a philosophical methodology of projection of generalizations from the organism's past observed behavior. It is consequently not reasonable to defend a thesis of methodological unity in any strong sense by an appeal to the fact that it can't be shown to be logically untenable.

There are no claims as difficult to refute as true claims, particularly tautologies, and metaphysical suggestions. As we have suggested, it is all too easy to find true things to say about scientific practice, and it is also easy to find things to say which may be retained through the vagaries of current practice by appeal to an idealized (and convenient) scientific future. The plain lesson of the evolutionary view is that an interesting philosophy of science with some bite for the analysis of actual theories will have to proceed at a rather low level of investigation, with careful examination of specimens and many tentative hypotheses.

Further Reading

General

A great deal of reading is required to know one's way about the literature of the philosophy of science. Much of this reading is not easy unless one knows some symbolic logic, some mathematics, or some relevant science. Occasionally, knowledge of all three is required. The beginning student must plunge into the middle of some quite difficult material. To help overcome the shock, it should be remembered that it is not necessary to understand everything that one reads word by word or sentence by sentence. At first, it is always useful to skim an article or book to see whether it is likely to prove valuable under closer scrutiny. Closer study is best undertaken after such a preliminary impression is gathered. One may quite sensibly conclude that further reading would prove valuable only if certain technical material is first mastered, or that points of interest can be gathered even if certain technical arguments are skipped over.

In the following recommendations, I have attempted to suggest literature that is relatively free from technical presuppositions, and which requires at most some detailed background in symbolic logic, a background often possessed by students of philosophy. In that sense, most of the recommendations constitute good entrance points to a wider range of literature, even if they are not always recognized classics in their fields. In obtaining a perspective on a book which seems initially somewhat unintelligible, it is often helpful to look up its reviews in the philosophical journals. By searching in particular through *The British Journal for the Philosophy of Science, The Journal of Philosophy, Mind, Philosophical Books, Philosophical Quarterly, Philosophical Review,* and *Philosophy of Science* for reviews of a book (they usually appear one to three years after the original publication date), a student can often find some general comments about the structure and the claims advanced in the book which may prove extremely valuable. The reviews are usually listed in an annual index bound with the journal, but one must be alert for valuable longer reviews and commentaries described under special rubrics such as "critical notices." Philosophers often allude to people and to views in a manner which is obvious to professional philosophers, but not to others. The reviews are a good way to discover allusions which may otherwise not be obvious.

Insofar as general philosophy of science refers to actual scientific practice, it is likely to allude to examples from physics and occasionally to examples from biology. These examples in turn frequently come from relativity theory, some branch of quantum theory, or from molecular biology. A philosopher of science should read as much scientific literature from as many areas of science as he can, if only the articles in *Scientific American* or *Science Journal.* Each year, Penguin paperbacks publishes a science survey series, and the journal *Nature* has begun to publish an annual science report. These sources are particularly interesting for source material at a non-specialist level as they attempt to assess rival theories on the basis of admittedly fresh and sometimes flatly contradictory data. In addition, series like *The Science Study Series* (Heinemann, London), *The World Universal Library* (Weidenfeld and Nicolson, London), *The Van Nostrand Momentum Books* (Van Nostrand, Princeton, New Jersey), *The*

Concepts of Modern Biology (Prentice-Hall, Englewood-Cliffs, New Jersey), and other paperback series are constantly being issued at a level of discussion which makes currently accepted scientific knowledge available to the non-specialist reader without papering over all of the crucial residual problems and known counter-examples facing majority views.

Chapter One

The following items from the bibliography are books written by scientists which contain interesting discussions about specific philosophical problems of scientific theorizing: [A13], [B6], [B8], [B13], [D1], [E3], [F4], [G6], [G8], [H4], [H5], [H10], [H13], [J1], [J2], [L3], [M1], [M2], [N3], [P1], [P2], [P3], [R1], [R3], [S3], [S9], [T6], [W2], and [W8]. Books which relate current scientific discoveries in an intelligent fashion to traditional philosophical and humanist concerns are not frequent. A biologist [C6] has an interesting discussion of problems which may be raised by irreversible scientific manipulations of our environment, and [P9] contains an intriguing discussion of space travel in a philosophical perspective.

Philosophers of science who stress that methodological analysis should enable one to distinguish sound science from counterfeit have rarely examined the odd and unusual books (which exist in abundance, but are ignored by the majority of academic scientists and philosophers) which are either brilliant or quite misguided. It is useful to look at books like [B11] and [K2] when thinking about the possibility of finding philosophical paradigms of sound scientific practice which rely solely on logical features of theories or of the relationship between theories and data.

Some attempts to study scientific practice in a quantitative manner without relying on normative principles supplied by philosophical analysis are provided by [P7] and [T7].

Chapter Two

The approach to philosophy of science discussed in this chapter is illustrated by [H2], [H3], [H11], [K6], [T4], and [T5]. One book [K6] has already become a classic and has had a great deal of influence on historians of scientific ideas. A great deal of fascinating exposition of modern physical theories along with philosophical analyses of their structure are contained in [H2] and [H11].

There are some philosophers of science who have coupled careful historical inquiry with the belief that general logical models can prove useful. These philosophers hold views which to some extent combine elements of the views discussed both in Chapter Two and in Chapter Three. An outstanding example is P. K. Feyerabend. See his important essays in volume II of [B2], in volume III of [C1], and in [C5]. The discussion of Feyerabend's paper in [C1] is quite useful in illustrating the difficulties facing a philosopher who attempts a somewhat eclectic position, no matter how reasonable it may seem.

Historians of science as such are not discussed in this book. As an example of acute historical scholarship coupled with a resolute refusal to generalize, one could do no better than to look at the essay and discussion by L. Pearce Williams in volume III of [L1].

The criteria for the viability of theories given in the chapter are an amalgam of ideas or variants on the ideas of a number of philosophers. K. R. Popper has been responsible for stressing the falsifiability criterion in modern philosophy of science, although the view sketched here differs somewhat from his treatment. See the discussions in [P5] and [P6]. Paradigm conservation is introduced and discussed in [K6] and in H. Putnam's essay in [S2], although these writers do not treat it as a criterion of viability. As a criterion of viability, paradigm conservation bears certain similarities to N. Goodman's notion of entrenchment as a criterion for systematic projection. See [A10] and [G5]. The significance criterion is a liberalized version of some ideas about scientific inference expressed in [A11], and traceable to ideas given in the references of that paper.

There are many philosophers who have based philosophies of science on views developed from the history of science, but whose philosophies do not easily fit the organizational framework of this book. In particular [P4] and [B15] can be mentioned because they reward an investigation. In [P4] there is a refusal to generalize about scientific practice along with an emphasis on personal intuition in science, which is a valuable source of perspective on more widely accepted views. In [B15] there is an introduction to A. N. Whitehead's philosophy of science, an extremely ingenious metaphysical system, which is too complex to summarize in any fashion in this monograph.

Chapter Three

The major difficulty in examining the literature offering discussion of various logical models is that much of it requires some considerable understanding of modern symbolic logic. This situation has been somewhat alleviated with the publication of [N2], an anthology of important papers which requires minimal logical sophistication, and which contains a valuable summarizing essay from the editor. There is in [N1] a very useful survey of a wide range of opinions which requires some logical expertise, but which can be read without mastering any particular logical system. Eight studies—[A1], [B10], [H6], [H9], [P5], [P6], [R5], and [S1]—present variants of the general view which has been called the hypothetico-deductive construal of theories, and treats axiomatization as an essential preliminary to any full analysis of scientific theories. Particularly useful, because of its searching exposition and treatment of the major views of other philosophers, is [S1].

Explanation patterns in logical models are carefully presented in [H6]. Hempel offers two patterns altogether: the deductive-nomological pattern mentioned in this chapter, and a statistical pattern required where statements in a theory contain probabilities. The original formulations of the deductive-nomological pattern, a pattern which is essential to explanation in the context of axiomatized theories in logical models, are criticized in [A6] and [E1]. Some particularly damaging criticisms are presented in [E1] which can be met only by adding such severe restrictions to the pattern that few scientific explanations met with in practice could meet revised models. This problem is also discussed in [A6] along with a model which is correctly stated in [A4]. In [S1] there is an extensive discussion of the role of explanation in logical models along with a detailed examination of various technical difficulties, and [C2] and [C3] contain frontal attacks on the suggestion that scientific explanations should be based on deductive connections between statements of a certain restricted kind.

Confirmatory patterns in logical models can also be studied in the relevant sections of [S1]. The paradox mentioned in the chapter is discussed in [S1], in [G4], and in J. L. Mackie's essay reprinted in [N2]. A monumental attempt to provide a general, quantitative confirmation function has been made by R. Carnap. The literature is best started from a reading of relevant portions of [S2], particularly J. Kemeny's article and Carnap's own statement of his position. A non-technical introductory account will be found in [A10], along with a survey of other philosophical ideas about confirmation. It is useful to look at [J2], which contains an account of scientific inference by a distinguished scientist which rightly stresses the importance of experimental error by contrast to many philosophical discussions. I have elaborated the suggestions made in the chapter about inference based on probability assessments in [A11], which should be taken as a full statement of the position only adumbrated in this chapter.

Chapter Four

An evolutionary view of the development of scientific practice has been sketched by a number of philosophers, notably T. S. Kuhn, K. R. Popper, and S. E. Toulmin. See [K6], [P5], and particularly [T3]. P. K. Feyerabend has repeatedly stressed the importance of generating a wide range of incompatible theories for governing sound scientific progress, a point of view quite close to major threads of the evolutionary view. See, in particular, his essay in volume III of [C1] as well as [F3].

Chapter Five

An excellent discussion of verificationism is to be found in *Part II: Significance,* pp. 127–225 of [S1]. But [H7] and [H9]

also contain very clear and interesting treatments of verificationism and Craig's Theorem, respectively. Also, [C7] and
[P10] should be consulted as references to Craig's Theorem.
Operationism is discussed explicitly in [S6] and [H11]. The
partial interpretation view of theoretical terms receives full
treatment in [A1] and [A2].

There are some amusing historical cases of the consequences
of basing views on data gathered at the limits of observability
in [L2]. I have tried to give a careful treatment of the problems of experimental error and the increasing precision of
measuring instruments with respect to the confirmation of
theories in [A3], which contains a fuller discussion of some of
the ideas mentioned in this chapter. There is in [K3] an in-
sightful discussion of the role of an idealized environment in
physical theory.

An extremely interesting example of the reworking of classical theories in a fixed-data environment so as to obtain a
better fit with a more elegant theory is provided by rational
mechanics. See [T6] and the essays by Noll, Truesdell, and
Grad in volume I of [B14]. This work should be very carefully contrasted with views which suggest that sound physical
discoveries must occur primarily in areas of research in which
new data provided by new measuring instruments are tne
major constraints on theorizing.

Chapter Six

A careful and comprehensive treatment of the literature
touching on philosophical issues of space and time up to 1963
is offered in [G10], but it is not easy reading. An extremely
stimulating treatment of certain topics is provided in [R2] and
[W6], although [G10] and [S10] may be usefully consulted for
a discussion of Reichenbach's and Whitrow's views.

For interesting scientific speculation about space and time
accessible to the non-specialist reader, one may look at [A13],
[B3], [B5], [G2], [G3], [L3], [N3], and [W5]; [G2] contains
some specialist papers, but the discussions are often fascinating.

The problems about irreversibility receive philosophical
examination in [G10], [S10], in Costa de Beauregard's essay in

[B1], and in H. Mehlberg's essay in [F1]. A brilliant but technical study is to be found in Grad's essay in [B14].

Determinism and causality are defined, somewhat differently, and explored philosophically in [B4], [B8], and [G10]. The views in this chapter were influenced by the definitions and discussion of [H12]. Open and closed systems and their significance receive explicit treatment in [H5] and in Havas' article in [B1]. The general relativistic explanations regarding the local significance of space-time frameworks and the incommensurability of time estimates of intervals made by different observers are given a non-technical treatment in [B3].

Descriptions of the two-slit experiment and other discoveries relevant to the apparent breakdown of spatio-temporal frameworks in microphysics can be found in [A13], [B4], [C1], (see articles by Sachs and Wallace) [C5], (see the article by Feyerabend) [F3]; and see [F4], [H1], [H2], [H11], [H13], and [P11].

The microphysical problem of measurement is discussed in detail in [A13], [B12], [C5] (see the article by Feyerabend), [E4], [F3], [H5], [J1], [K5] (see articles by Feyerabend and Süssman), [P11], [S3], [S5], [W9], and [W11]. There are non-orthodox approaches to measurement and to the significance of current microphysical theory to be found in [B4], and in [K5]; see articles by Bohm and Vigier. In [H2] is a discussion of non-orthodox approaches from an orthodox viewpoint. These controversies are philosophically and scientifically important, but the non-orthodox views have not been developed here because the controversies are highly technical, and philosophical reductionism is not supported by the non-orthodox theories.

Chapter Seven

It is so difficult to find bibliography on the philosophy of biology (and higher levels of analysis) that I have listed a number of references of interest to the general reader: [A5], [A8], [A9], [B9], [B13], [B15], [D1], [E2], [E3], [G7], [G8], [H4], [H10], [K1], [L2], [L4], [L5], [M1], [M2], [O1], [P1],

[P2], [P4], [R1], [R3], [R5], [S7], [S8], [T1], [T2], [V1], [W1], [W3], [W4], and [W10].

The material in [H4], [R1], and [R3] will serve to provide an interesting background to biological theorizing and its relationship to experimental data. In addition, [S8] is an interesting account of the history of the study of biological problems from a physical perspective.

An explicit account of logical models for reduction is to be found in [K4], and its bibliography. Discussions of reduction which are sympathetic to certain reductionist proposals occur in [H6] and [S6].

The theory of self-reproducing automata has an extensive bibliography in [V1]. Explicit attempts to suggest an ontology of levels can be found in [E3] and [W1]. Pattee's essay in [W1] is a brilliant attempt to fix some well-defined problems in the relationship of physical theories to biological observations. Homogeneous classes are introduced in [E3], and there is some further discussion of them in [A9]. In [A5], I have stated more fully the view about human consciousness sketched in this chapter, and have provided some reasons why consciousness, rather than intentional behavior conceived as a logical criterion, may be the essential element in mental life.

An Overview

In view of the fact that the reader may not be pursuing an academic course where he can obtain such guidance, I have made bold to suggest three comprehensive booklists which will provide overviews of varying intensity into the literature of contemporary philosophy of science.

The Three-Foot Philosophy of Science Bookshelf: [A10], [A11], [A13], [B3], [B9], [B13], [B14], [C4], [E3], [F4], [G4], [G10], [H2],]H8], [H11], [K6], [L2], [L4], [L5], [N2], [N3], [P4], [P5], [P7], [S1], [S2], [S6], [T1], [T6], [W1], and [W2].

The One-Foot Philosophy of Science Bookshelf: [A10], [B14], [C4], [F4], [G4], [G10], [H2], [K6], [N2], [S1], and [W1].

The Six-Inch Philosophy of Science Bookshelf: [A13], [E3], [H3], [K6], and [S1].

Bibliography

Series are marked on the left with an asterisk, and a publication date for the first volume is cited. Following an informal recent bibliographic practice, only minimal information has been provided along with correct authors, names, and titles for books currently in print which are listed in the bibliography. Most of these books appear in various editions in the United States and in England, frequently in at least one paperback form. If they cannot be located in smaller libraries, they may be easily traced through cumulative indices or lists of books in print for the past few years.

[A1]   Achinstein, P. *Concepts of Science* (Baltimore, 1968).

[A2]   Achinstein, P. "Theoretical Terms and Partial Interpretation," *The British Journal for the Philosophy of Science, 14* (1963–1964), pp. 89–105.

[A3]   Ackermann, R. J. "Confirmatory Models of Theories," *The British Journal for the Philosophy of Science, 16* (1965–1966), pp. 312–326.

[A4]   Ackermann, R. J., and Stenner, A. J. "A Corrected Model of Explanation," *Philosophy of Science, 33* (1966), pp. 168–171.

[A5]   Ackermann, R. J. "Explanations of Human Action," *Dialogue, 6* (1967), pp. 18–28.

[A6]   Ackermann, R. J. "Deductive Scientific Explanation," *Philosophy of Science, 32* (1965), pp. 155–167.

[A7]   Ackermann, R. J. "Inductive Simplicity," *Philosophy of Science, 28* (1961), pp. 152–161.

[A8]   Ackermann, R. J. "Mechanism and the Philosophy of Biology," *The Southern Journal of Philosophy, 6* (1968), pp. 143–151.

[A9]   Ackermann, R. J. "Mechanism, Methodology, and Biological Theory," *Synthese* (forthcoming).

[A10]   Ackermann, R. J. *Nondeductive Inference* (London, 1966).

[A11]   Ackermann, R. J. "Some Problems of Inductive Logic," in *Philosophical Logic,* Davis, J. W. (ed.) (forthcoming).

[A12]   Agassi, J. "Towards an Historiography of Science," *History and Theory,* Beiheft 2 (1963).

[A13]   Andrade e Silva, J., and Lochak, G. *Quanta* (London, 1969).

[B1]   Bar-Hillel, Y. (ed.). *Logic, Methodology, and Philosophy of Science* (Amsterdam, 1965).

*[B2]   Baumrin, B. (ed.). *Philosophy of Science, The Delaware Seminar,* 2 volumes (New York, 1963).

[B3]   Bergmann, P. G. *The Riddle of Gravitation* (New York, 1968).

[B4]   Bohm, D. *Causality and Chance in Modern Physics* (Harper Paperback, 1961).

[B5]   Bohm, D. "Problems in the Basic Concepts of Physics," (Birkbeck College, London, Inaugural Lecture, 1963).

[B6]   Bondi, H. *Assumption and Myth in Physical Theory* (Cambridge, England, 1967).

[B7]   Born, M. *Experiment and Theory in Physics* (Dover Paperback, 1956).

[B8]   Born, M. *Natural Philosophy of Cause and Chance* (Dover Paperback, 1964).

[B9]   Bower, T. G. R. "Slant Perception and Shape Constancy in Infants," *Science, 151* (1966), pp. 832–834.

[B10]   Braithwaite, R. B. *Scientific Explanation* (Cambridge, 1953).

[B11]   Branfield, W. *Continuous Creation* (London, 1950).

[B12]   Bub, J. "Hidden Variables and the Copenhagen Interpretation—A Reconciliation," *The British Journal for the Philosophy of Science, 19* (1968), pp. 185–210.

[B13]   Buckley, W. *Sociology and Modern Systems Theory* (Englewood Cliffs, 1967).

*[B14] Bunge, M. (ed.). *Delaware Seminar in the Foundations of Physics* (Berlin, 1967).

[B15]   Burgers, J. M. *Experience and Conceptual Activity* (Cambridge, Massachusetts, 1965).

*[C1]   Cohen, R. S., and Wartofsky, M. W., (eds.). *Boston Studies in the Philosophy of Science,* 3 volumes (New York, 1963).

[C2]   Collins, A. W. "Explanation and Causality," *Mind, 75* (1966), pp. 482–500.

[C3]   Collins, A. W. "The Use of Statistics in Explanation," *The*

British Journal for the Philosophy of Science, 17 (1966), pp. 127–140.

[C4]   Colodny, R. G., (ed.), *Beyond the Edge of Certainty: Essays in Contemporary Science and Philosophy* (New York, 1965).

[C5]   Colodny, R. G. (ed.). *Frontiers of Science and Philosophy* (Pittsburgh, 1962).

[C6]   Commoner, B. *Science and Survival* (New York, 1967).

[C7]   Craig, W. "Replacement of Auxiliary Expressions," *Philosophical Review, 55* (1956), pp. 38–55.

[D1]   Deutsch, J. A. *The Structure of Behavior* (Chicago, 1960).

[E1]   Eberle, R., Kaplan, D., and Montague, R. "Hempel and Oppenheim on Explanation," *Philosophy of Science, 28* (1961), pp. 418–428.

[E2]   Eden, M., and Kolers, P. A. (eds.). *Recognizing Patterns* (Cambridge, Massachusetts, 1968).

[E3]   Elsasser, W. *Atom and Organism* (Princeton, 1966).

[E4]   Everett, H. "'Relative State' Formulation of Quantum Mechanics," *Reviews of Modern Physics, 29* (1957), pp. 454–462.

[F1]   Feigl, H., and Maxwell, G. (eds.). *Current Issues in the Philosophy of Science* (New York, 1961).

*[F2]   Feigl, H., Maxwell, G., and Scriven M. (eds.). *Minnesota Studies in the Philosophy of Science,* 3 volumes (Minneapolis, 1956).

[F3]   Feyerabend, P. K. "On a Recent Critique of Complementarity," *Philosophy of Science, 35* (1968), pp. 309–331, and *36* (1969), pp. 82–105.

[F4]   Feynman, R. *The Character of Physical Law* (Cambridge, Massachusetts, 1965).

[G1]   Gale, R. M. *The Language of Time* (London, 1968).

[G2]   Gold, T. "Cosmic Processes and the Nature of Time," from *Mind and Cosmos,* edited by R. G. Colodny (Pittsburgh, 1966), pp. 311–329.

[G3]   Gold, T. (ed.). *The Nature of Time* (Cornell, 1967).

[G4]   Good, I. J. "The Paradox of Confirmation," *The British Journal for the Philosophy of Science, 11* (1960), pp. 145–148; *12* (1961), pp. 63–64; and *17* (1967), p. 322.

[G5]   Goodman, N. *Fact, Fiction, and Forecast* (Cambridge, Massachusetts, 1955).

[G6]   Gouiran, R. *Particles and Accerleators* (London, 1967).

[G7]   Grene, M. "Biology and the Problem of Levels of Reality," *New Scholasticism, 41* (1967), pp. 427–449.

[G8]   Griffith, J. S. *A View of the Brain* (Oxford, 1967).

[G9]   Grünbaum, A. *Modern Science and Zeno's Paradoxes* (Middletown, 1967).

[G10] Grünbaum, A. *Philosophical Problems of Space and Time* (New York, 1963).

[H1] Hacking, I. *The Logic of Statistical Inference* (Cambridge, England, 1965).

[H2] Hanson, N. R. *The Concept of the Positron* (Cambridge, England, 1963).

[H3] Hanson, N. R. *Patterns of Discovery* (Cambridge, England, 1958).

[H4] Harris, H. *Nucleus and Cytoplasm* (Oxford, 1968).

[H5] Havas, P. "Causality Requirements and the Theory of Relativity," *Synthese, 18* (1968), pp. 75–102.

[H6] Hempel, C. G. *Aspects of Scientific Explanation and Other Essays in the Philosophy of Science* (New York, 1965).

[H7] Hempel, C. G. "The Concept of Cognitive Significance: A Reconsideration," *Proceedings of the American Academy of Arts and Sciences, 80* (1951), pp. 61–77.

[H8] Hempel, C. G. "Inductive Inconsistencies," *Synthese, 12* (1960), pp. 439–469.

[H9] Hempel, C. G. "The Theoretician's Dilemma," Volume II of [F2], pp. 37–98.

[H10] Herskowitz, I. *Basic Principles of Molecular Genetics* (London, 1967).

[H11] Hesse, M. *Forces and Fields* (London, 1961).

[H12] Hillinger, C. "A Generalization of the Principle of Causality, Which Makes it Applicable to Evolutionary Systems," *Synthese, 18* (1968), pp. 68–74.

[H13] Hoffmann, B. *The Strange Story of the Quantum* (Pelican Books, 1963).

[H14] Humphreys, W. C. *Anomalies and Scientific Theories* (San Francisco, 1968).

[J1] Jammer, M. *The Conceptual Development of Quantum Mechanics* (New York, 1966).

[J2] Jeffreys, H. *Scientific Inference* (Cambridge, England, 1931).

[K1] Kaplan, M. M., and Moorhead, P. S. (eds.). "Mathematical Challenges to the Neo-Darwinian Interpretation of Evolution," *Wistar Institute Monograph No. 5* (Philadelphia, 1967).

[K2] Kapp, R. O. *Towards a Unified Cosmology* (London, 1960).

[K3] Kilmister, C. W. *The Environment in Physics* (London, 1965).

[K4] Kim, J. "Reduction, Correspondence, and Identity," *The Monist, 52* (1968), pp. 424–438.

[K5] Körner, S. (ed.). *Observation and Interpretation* (London, 1957).

[K6] Kuhn, T. S. *The Structure of Scientific Revolutions* (Chicago, 1962).

*[L1] Lakatos, I., and Musgrave, A. (eds.). *Proceedings of the International Colloquium in the Philosophy of Science, London, 1965,* 3 volumes complete (Amsterdam, 1968).

[L2]   Large, E. C. *The Advance of the Fungi* (Dover Paperback, 1940).

[L3]   Livingston, M. S. *Particle Physics* (New York, 1968).

[L4]   Lorenz, K. "Gestalt Perception as Fundamental to Scientific Knowledge," *General Systems Yearbook, 7* (1962), pp. 37–56.

[L5]   Lorenz, K. "Kant's Doctrine of the A Priori in the Light of Contemporary Biology," *General Systems Yearbook, 7* (1962), pp. 23–35.

[M1]   Margalef, R. *Perspectives in Ecological Theory* (Chicago, 1968).

[M2]   Mehrabian, A. *An Analysis of Personality Theories* (Englewood Cliffs, 1968).

[N1]   Nagel, E. *The Structure of Science* (New York, 1961).

[N2]   Nidditch, P. H. *The Philosophy of Science* (Oxford, 1968).

[N3]   North, J. D. *The Measure of the Universe* (Oxford, 1965).

[O1]   Orme, J. F. *Time, Experience, and Behavior* (London, 1969).

[P1]   Pantin, C. F. A. *The Relations Between the Sciences* (Cambridge, England, 1968).

[P2]   Pattee, H. H. "The Physical Basis of Coding and Reliability in Biological Function," [W1], pp. 67–93.

[P3]   Petersen, A. *Quantum Physics and the Philosophical Tradition* (Cambridge, Massachusetts, 1968).

[P4]   Polanyi, M. *Personal Knowledge: Towards a Post-Critical Philosophy* (London, 1958).

[P5]   Popper, K. R. *Conjectures and Refutations* (London, 1963).

[P6]   Popper, K. R. *The Logic of Scientific Discovery* (London, 1959).

[P7)   Price, D. *Little Science, Big Science* (Columbia, New York, 1963).

[P8]   Prior, A. N. *Papers on Time and Tense* (Oxford, 1968).

[P9]   Puccetti, R. *Persons* (London, 1968).

[P10] Putnam, H. "Craig's Theorem," *The Journal of Philosophy, 62* (1965), pp. 251–260.

[P11] Putnam, H. "A Philosopher Looks at Quantum Mechanics," [C4], pp. 75–101.

[R1]   Ramsay, J. A. *The Experimental Basis of Modern Biology* (Cambridge, 1965).

[R2]   Reichenbach, H. *Space and Time* (Dover Paperback, 1958).

[R3]   Roeder, K. D. *Nerve Cells and Insect Behavior* (Cambridge, Massachusetts, 1963).

[R4]   Rogers, B. "On Discrete Spaces," *The American Philosophical Quarterly, 5* (1968), pp. 117–123.

[R5]   Rudner, R. S. *Philosophy of Social Science* (New York, 1966).

[S1]   Scheffler, I. *The Anatomy of Inquiry* (London, 1964).

[S2]   Schilpp, P. A. (ed.). *The Philosophy of Rudolf Carnap* (LaSalle, 1963).

[S3]   Schlegel, R. *Completeness in Science* (New York, 1967).

[S4]   Schrödinger, E. *What is Life?* (Cambridge, England, 1944).

[S5]   Shimony, A. "Role of the Observer in Quantum Theory," *American Journal of Physics, 31* (1963), pp. 755–773.

[S6]   Smart, J. J. C. *Between Science and Philosophy* (New York, 1968).

[S7]   Sperry, R. W. "Neurology and the Mind-Brain Problem," *American Scientist, 40* (1952), pp. 291–312.

[S8]   Stent, G. S. "That Was the Molecular Biology that Was," *Science, 160* (1968), pp. 390–395.

[S9]   Stewart, A. T. *Perpetual Motion* (London, 1965).

[S10]   Swinburne, R. *Space and Time* (London, 1968).

[T1]   Taylor, C. *The Explanation of Behaviour* (London, 1964).

[T2]   Taylor, C. "Neutrality in Political Science," pp. 25–57 of P. Laslett and W. G. Runciman (eds.). *Philosophy, Politics, and Society, Series Three* (Oxford, 1967).

[T3]   Toulmin, S. "Conceptual Revolutions in Science," [C1], volume III, pp. 331–347.

[T4]   Toulmin, S. *Foresight and Understanding* (London, 1961).

[T5]   Toulmin, S. *The Philosophy of Science* (London, 1953).

[T6]   Truesdell, C. *Six Lectures on Modern Natural Philosophy* (Berlin, 1966).

[T7]   Tullock, G. *The Organization of Inquiry* (Durham, 1966).

[V1]   Von Neumann, J. *Theory of Self-Reproducing Automata,* A. W. Burks (ed.) (Urbana, 1966).

*[W1]   Waddington, C. H. (ed.). *Towards a Theoretical Biology,* 1 volume (another expected shortly) (Edinburgh, 1968).

[W2]   Watson, W. H. *Understanding Physics Today* (Cambridge, England, 1967).

[W3]   Wells, M. *Lower Animals* (London, 1968).

[W4]   Went, F. W. "The Size of Man," *American Scientist, 56* (1968), pp. 400–413.

[W5]   Wheeler, J. A. "Our Universe: The Known and the Unknown," *American Scientist, 56* (1968), pp. 1–20.

[W6]   Whitrow, G. J. *The Natural Philosophy of Time* (Harper Paperback, 1963).

[W7]   Whitrow, G. J. "Why Physical Space Has Three Dimensions," *General Systems Yearbook, 7* (1962), pp. 121–129.

[W8]   Whittaker, E. *From Euclid to Eddington* (Dover Paperback, 1958).

[W9]   Wigner, E. P. "The Problem of Measurement," *American Journal of Physics, 31* (1963), pp. 6–15.

[W10]   Winch, P. *The Idea of a Social Science* (London, 1958).

[W11]   Witmer, E. E. "Interpretation of Quantum Mechanics and the Future of Physics," *American Journal of Physics, 35* (1967), pp. 40–52.

Index

(Names appearing in *Further Reading* and the *Bibliography* are not cited in the Index.)

Ackermann, R. J., 53
adaptation, 64–68, 92, 97
axiomatic systems, construal of theories as, 44, 68, 83–88, 98, 132

Bayes' Theorem, 52, 53
Bower, T. G. R., 96
Bridgman, P. W., 80
Bub, J., 99

causal theories, 108–114
closed systems, 105–127, 138
common sense, 18, 19, 22
concepts, 116, 146, 147
confirmation, 43–58, 88–91, 155: paradox of, 49–52
consciousness, 146, 147
context of justification, 42
Craig's Theorem, 84–86, 94, 95, 156
criticism, literary or musical, 22–24

data environment, 66, 69, 70, 87–97, 107, 135, 147, 156
determinism, 103–114, 139–146, 157

environment, 118, 119, 138
epistemology, 17, 20, 79, 80

ethology, 95–97
experimental error, 87–91, 156
explanation, 43–51, 154, 155

falsifiability, 30–34, 48, 57, 67, 89, 153

Goedel's Theorem, 119

Hanson, N. R., 28, 36
homogeneous class, 147, 148, 158
hypotheses, 33, 41–44

ideal cases, 31, 32
indeterministic mechanism, 140–147

Kelly, J. C., v, xi
Kuhn, T. S., 28

language, ordinary, 20, 21
laws, 33, 41–46
Lone Ranger, The, 28, 29

Mach, Ernst, 80
measurement, 104–107, 125–129, 157
models, logical, 20–23, 28, 42–47, 53, 55, 72, 78, 89, 154, 155

normative, philosophy of science as, 15, 16, 152

objectivity, 55, 58–66
observation, 46, 59, 60, 87, 93–95, 104–106
operationism, 78–82, 124, 125, 156

paradigm conservation, 36–39, 40, 52, 57, 67, 153
partial interpretation, 82–86
philosophy, scope of, 25
physical, 128, 129
Plato, 97

Ramsay, J. A., 99
rationality, 55–58, 60, 65
reduction, 77, 111, 113, 127–143, 158
reversibility, temporal, 111–116, 127, 131, 152, 156, 157

Schrödinger, E., 125
science, aim of, 21–23, 29

significance, 34–36, 51, 52, 57, 67, 68, 153
simplicity, 43, 44
space, Chapter 6, *passim,* 156, 157: perceptual, 119, 120

theories, 33, 41, 44, 46, 64–70, 87–100, 103–114, 132, 157: axiomatic construal of, 44, 68, 83–88, 98, 132, causal, 108–114, 157, deterministic, 103–114, 139–146, 157, reversible, 111–116, 127, 131, 152, 156, 157
time, Chapter 6, *passim,* 156, 157
Toulmin, S., 28
two-slit experiment, 121–127, 157

verificationism, 78–86, 155, 156
viability, 30–39
von Neumann, J., 117

Zeno's Paradox, 136